KNOWLEDGE
AND WONDER

VICTOR F. WEISSKOPF

KNOWLEDGE

AND WONDER

The Natural World as Man Knows it

". . . for all knowledge and wonder (which is the seed of knowledge) is an impression of pleasure in itself . . ."

FRANCIS BACON

DOUBLEDAY & COMPANY, INC.
Garden City, New York
1962

First Edition

Illustrations by R. Paul Larkin

TABLE OF CONTENTS

PLATE ACKNOWLEDGMENTS

Plates I and XI. Mt. Wilson and Palomar Observatories

Plate II. Valasek, *Introduction to Theoretical and Experimental Optics,* John Wiley & Sons, New York, 1949.

Plate III. Courtesy: Erwin W. Müller and Paul Weller

Plate IV. H. Raether, "Elektroninterferenzen," Handbuch der Physik, Vol. 32, Springer, Berlin (1957)

Plate V. H. E. White, *Physical Review,* Vol. 37, 1416 (1931)

Plate VI. E. Kellenberger, A. Ryter and J. Sèchaud, *J. Biophysical and Biochemical Cytology,* Vol. 4, 671 (1958)

Plate VII. A. Rich, *Reviews of Modern Physics,* Vol. 31, 193 (1959)

Plate VIII. A. Kleinschmidt (Frankfurt) 111th International Congress of Surface Activity, Cologne, 1960, Vol. II, 138

Plate IX. E. Kellenberger and J. Bron

Plate X. E. Kellenberger and W. Arber, *Zeitschrift für Naturforschung,* Vol. 106, 698 (1955)

PREFACE

This book had its beginning in a series of lectures the author gave at the Buckingham School in Cambridge, Massachusetts, before an audience with no special grounding in science. The idea was to sketch our present scientific understanding of natural phenomena and to try to show the universality of that understanding and its human significance.

Now such an undertaking runs into difficulties that are only too well known. Scientific knowledge is hard to communicate to the non-scientist; there is so much to be explained before one can come to the essential point. All too often the layman cannot see the forest, but only the trees. The difficulties, however, should not prevent, or even discourage, scientists from tackling the job in different ways. This book is one way of giving the uninitiated an idea of the greatest cultural achievement of our time.

Today the different natural sciences are no longer independent of each other. Chemistry, physics, geology, astronomy and biology are all linked together, and all are treated in this book, though some at greater length than the others. Physics, being the basis of all the natural sciences, gets the main emphasis—in particular, atomic physics since everything in Nature is made of atoms. What is stressed in the book is the trend toward universality in science, from the elementary atomic particle to the living world, a common point of view whose realization seems nearer because of the enormous progress the last few decades have brought in our understanding of atoms, stars and the living cell.

In writing a book as small as this one, the author must make a selection and necessarily will have to leave out many important topics. The choice was based upon the author's own views of the importance of various fields and, to no small extent, upon his restricted knowledge. There is one omission that needs some comment. Einstein's Theory of Relativity is not included and is scarely mentioned. There is no question in the author's mind that the Einstein theory is one of the greatest achievements of physics and of all science. It has revolutionized our ideas of space and time to such an extent that without Einstein no exact quantitative consideration of space and time is possible. Einstein's ideas, therefore, play a decisive rôle in the *quantitative* formulation of many scientific problems. This book, however, emphasizes the *qualitative* aspects of the picture of the world seen in science. Relativity theory is not absolutely necessary to this view, and we have left it out of our discussion.

The author received help from many people who read the early versions of the manuscript and suggested changes and additions. He is deeply indebted to his fellow scientists David Hawkins, Mervyn Hine, Philip Morrison, Alex Rich, and Cyril Smith. He derived much stimulation from the book *Physics* edited by the Physical Science Study Committee (D. C. Heath and Co., 1960). He also wants to express his particular gratitude to two non-scientists, Kingman Brewster and Ann Morrison, for their help as guinea pigs in the early samplings, and for their constant encouragement throughout. Special thanks go to Mr. John H. Durston, of Educational Services Incorporated, for his careful revision and his improvements in the manuscript, to Mr. R. Paul Larkin for his illustrations, and to the Buckingham School, whose invitation to lecture brought this book into being.

Victor F. Weisskopf

Geneva, Switzerland
March 1, 1962

KNOWLEDGE
AND WONDER

OUR PLACE IN SPACE

Chapter One

How large is the world? How large are the objects about us in this world? We have an immediate feeling for the size of the objects with which we deal in our daily life. The smallest length our eyes can perceive is the breadth of a hair; it is about a tenth of a millimeter[1] across. The human body is roughly two meters high; that is a little more than ten thousand times larger than the breadth of a hair. Other objects about us, such as furniture, tools, cars, houses, are all of roughly the same size as our body; if this were not so, we could not handle them easily.

When we look out the window at the landscape, we see objects of greater size and distance, such as mountains and plains. We can get an idea of the distances involved by counting the steps necessary

[1] We are going to measure all distances in the metric system as all scientists do, and also as ordinary people do in most countries except England and the United States. The introduction of this useful system in Europe is one of the positive effects of the French Revolution; it is deplorable that this custom did not take hold in the English-speaking nations.

The unit of length is a meter, a little more than three feet, approximately the distance between the tip of the nose to the tip of the fingers of an outstretched arm. According to the scientific definition of the founders of this system, the meter should have been one forty millionth of the circumference of the earth. They did not measure things too accurately at that time and made a very small error. We now stick to their original meter. A centimeter is a hundredth of a meter; it is roughly equal to the diameter of a dime. A millimeter is a thousandth of a meter; it is approximately equal to the thickness of a dime. A kilometer, one thousand meters, is a "lean" mile, 3300 feet.

to reach them—that is, by comparing them directly with our body. We find that the objects we can see in the distance—the mountains, hills and forests—are only a few kilometers away, not more than 100 even for the towering Rocky Mountains.

Here ends our direct perception of distance. It would be too hard to measure a continent, not to say the Earth, by counting steps. Hence we must use indirect methods for getting an idea of the sizes and distances larger than, say, 100 kilometers. One method is the measurement of distance by speed. If I travel from one point to another at a given speed, say 100 kilometers per hour, and know the time it took, I can figure the distance. Modern means of transportation have made it easy. An airplane takes about ten minutes to travel 100 kilometers; it takes about 500 minutes to fly from coast to coast. Hence the size of our continent is about 5000 kilometers. It would take the same airplane almost ten times longer to fly around the world; hence the circumference of the Earth should be about 50,000 kilometers. Actually it is 40,000 kilometers. Since we know that the Earth is a sphere, it is easy to figure the diameter from the circumference—13,000 kilometers. This is the size of our own abode, the planet Earth.

THE DISTANCE OF THE MOON, THE SUN, AND THE PLANETS

Now we turn our attention to the heavenly bodies. How can we measure their distance and size? The Sun, the Moon, and the stars seem all to be pinned on some domelike surface enclosing the space in which we live. When we look at the starry sky, it is as if all the heavenly bodies were at the same distance from us. (See Figure 1.) The actual distance of these bodies is too vast to be directly perceived.

But there are very simple ways of measuring the distance of the closer heavenly bodies. The simplest method is a very new one based upon the recent advances in radar technique. One directs a beam of radar at the object and sends off a short signal. One waits for the return of the reflected radar wave and measures the time elapsed between emission and return of the signal. When the signal is aimed at the moon, the elapsed time interval has been found to be 2.6

Figure 1. Woodcut from the Middle Ages showing the prevailing idea of the system of the world. The traveler puts his head through the vault of the sky and discovers the complexities which move the stars.

seconds. It took the radar signal that long to travel to the moon and return. The radar wave is a kind of light wave, and all light travels at the same speed[2]—300,000 kilometers per second. We therefore conclude that the distance Earth-Moon-Earth is $2.6 \times$ 300,000 kilometers, which tells us that the Moon is about 400,000 kilometers away. This is again a distance measurement by speed.

And how large is the Moon, now that we know its distance? We see the Moon in the form of a disk. Its size is such that it would take 360 disks like it, side by side, to make a big circle from the horizon west up to the zenith and down to the horizon east. Since we know the distance of the Moon, we also know the length of this

[2] See Chapter Three.

half circle whose radius is the distance of the Moon. It is pi times the radius, or pi times 400,000 kilometers. The diameter of the Moon must be 1/360 of this length, and this is 3600 kilometers. It is a third the size of the Earth, and the distance to the Moon is only a little more than thirty times the diameter of the Earth. Our Moon is almost a terrestrial object.

Let us now look at other heavenly objects, but first only at the members of our solar system, the Sun and the other planets. Men have observed the motions of the planets for many centuries and have wondered what they signified. Since the days of Copernicus it has been clear that the strange movements of the planets are the motions of bodies orbiting in circles (actually ellipses, which are almost circles) around the Sun as we see them from the Earth, which also circles the Sun. The Earth is one of the planets, the third one when the orbits are counted from the Sun out. Careful observation of the motions as seen from the Earth reveals the relative sizes of the orbits of different planets. For example, Mercury always is observed close to the Sun and never farther away from it than 23 degrees; from this fact we conclude that the radius of Mercury's orbit is 0.38, or a bit more than one third, of the radius of the orbit of the Earth. In the same way we find that Venus's orbit is 0.7 of the Earth's, or a little more than two thirds. Thus we can construct a picture of the solar system in the right proportions, but we do not know its actual size. (See Figure 2.)

But how do we find the size of these orbits and then obtain an idea of the true dimensions of the solar system? Since we know the positions of all the members of the solar system relative to each other, we need only to measure the true distance of one of them in order to find the true dimensions of all orbits. Here again we can use the radar method of measuring distances within the solar system.

Although some promising experiments have been made, we have not yet been able, at this writing, to use the radar beam technique to obtain useful measurements of the distance from the Earth to the Sun. We can, however, direct our radar beam to one of the nearby planets. This has been done with Venus, and the time between emission and return of the signal was somewhere between five and fifteen minutes, depending upon where in their orbits the Earth and Venus happened to be at the times of observation. From the speed of light we can figure out that the distance to Venus is of the order of millions of kilo-

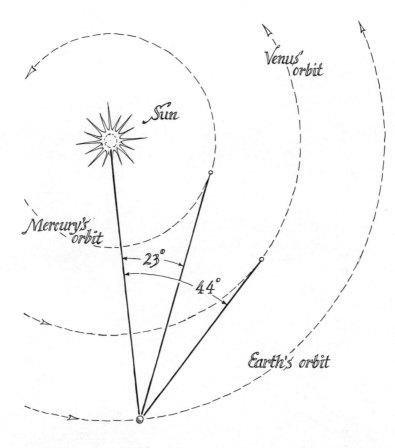

Figure 2. The largest angles at which we see Mercury and Venus away from the sun. They determine the ratios between the Earth's orbit and the orbits of Mercury and Venus.

meters. Thus we have found a distance characteristic of the solar system. The size of the solar system is such that light takes minutes to travel from one planet to the other. Once we have determined one single distance such as Venus-Earth, it is no longer difficult to find any other distance in the solar system, since we know the proportions and the relative sizes of the orbits. Right away we can find the distance that is most important for us here on Earth, the distance Sun-Earth. It turns out to be 150 million kilometers; light takes a little more than eight minutes to travel from the Sun to us.

How big is the Sun? It appears to be as large as the Moon, but it is, as we can easily figure out, 375 times farther away. Hence the diameter of the Sun must be 375 times larger than the Moon, and that multiplication gives 1.4 million kilometers. The Sun is more than a hundred times larger than the Earth. (See Figure 3.)

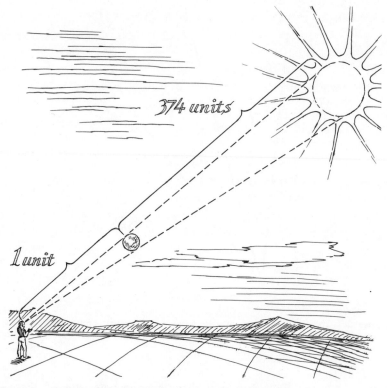

Figure 3. Relationship of moon and sun to Earth observer.

THE DISTANCE OF THE STARS

We have now measured the size of our solar system, which, better than the planet Earth alone, deserves to be called our abode. After all, the Sun is our main source of light, warmth, and energy. It is the star to which we belong and it is part of our life. The solar system is the world in which we live. Let us look outside.

All we see there are stars. They are called "fixed stars" because they seem to be immovable in contrast to the planets, whose motion around the Sun is plainly visible. Actually the stars are "fixed" only because they are so far away that any motion they might have would be too slow to observe within a lifetime. In fact they do move. Exact photographs of the sky show slight changes in the positions of stars over periods of many years. We can infer from ancient scriptures that some of the stellar constellations looked quite different many thousand years ago.

But how far are they away? Let us make an assumption which to a great extent turns out to be correct—that the stars we see in the sky are all about as luminous and as large as the Sun. Actually the stars do not appear to be equally bright; there are bright ones and weak ones. If our assumption is correct, this can only be due to the fact that some are farther away and some are nearer. We then can easily calculate the distance of a star.

Let us look at Sirius, for example, in relation to a well-known fact: If one of two equally bright light sources is n times farther away than the other, the nearer one appears n^2 times brighter than the farther one. Let us apply this law to Sirius and the Sun. The Sun appears much brighter than Sirius. If we compare the light intensities, we find that the Sun is a (million)^2 times brighter than the bright star Sirius. Hence it follows from our law that Sirius must be a million times farther away than the Sun! Other stars, such as the seven stars of the Big Dipper, are about nine times weaker than Sirius. So they must be about three times farther away if our assumption of equal luminosity is correct. It would be easy to find the distances of all stars, and thus the size of our visible universe, if it were correct that most of the stars are about equally luminous.

Can we check this hypothesis by some other observations? Yes, we can. We do it by measuring directly the distance of some stars and then comparing the result with the result from our hypothesis. If they agree, our hypothesis is correct. The simplest method to measure the distance of an object beyond reach is to look at it from two different points and note the change of direction in which it appears. A distant tree will be seen in a slightly different direction if I walk a few steps in a direction perpendicular to the line between me and the tree. The farther the tree is away from me, the smaller is this change. The distance of the tree can be calculated from that change of direction.[3] Of course the stars are so far away that we cannot observe the slightest change of direction when looking at a star from different locations on Earth. But we can make use of the fact that the Earth circles around the Sun and that we therefore are changing our point of observation all the time (See Figure 4.)

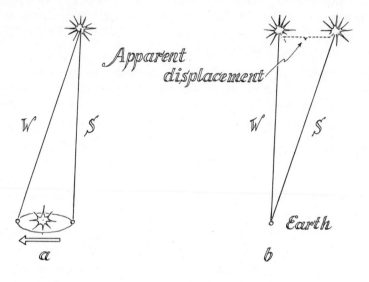

Figure 4. Apparent displacement. In winter the star is seen in the direction W and in summer in the direction S as shown in (a). Seen from the Earth, the star therefore appears displaced by a distance equal to the diameter of the Earth orbit as seen in (b).

In the winter, in fact, we are looking at the stars from a spot 300 million kilometers away from the spot where we look at the stars in the summer. When we move from one point of the circle to the opposite point, the stars, in particular the nearer ones, should appear slightly shifted. When the Earth has moved, say, from right to left during the half year, the star should have moved from left to right relative to the background. In fact, the star has moved across the sky a distance that equals the diameter of the Earth's orbit (300 million kilometers) as the orbit would appear to a viewer as far away as the star. If our previous hypothesis is right, Sirius, being then a million times farther away than the Sun, should be found to perform small periodic displacements not larger than a dime would appear to

[3] If I express the change of direction in degrees, say a degrees, and if I walk n meters, the distance of the tree is $57 \times n/a$. The smaller a, the larger the distance.

be when viewed at a distance of five kilometers (a million times the radius of the dime). These displacements actually have been found!

About 125 years ago the astronomers had instruments to measure such small changes in position, and it turned out that Sirius and the other stars as bright as Sirius are really about as far away as they should be when we assume that they are about as luminous as the Sun. Whenever the distance of a star could be measured by its small periodic displacement, it turned out that the brightest stars are the nearest and the fainter stars are farther away. Our hypothesis was proved to be roughly correct. Most stars whose distance could be determined were not very different in their actual light intensity.

We now know the distance of the brightest, and therefore the nearest, stars. We can judge the amount of empty space between our solar system and the next sunlike object—a million times the distance Earth-Sun, or about 10^{14} kilometers.[4] The light takes ten years to travel this distance, and this is why we measure distances of that order in light-years: Sirius is ten light-years away. Compare this with the few minutes which light takes to travel within the solar system or with the fact that light needs only one tenth of a second to travel around the Earth, and you get an idea of the distance to our nearest sister suns.

There are not many stars whose distance can be measured with the displacement method—only the ones that are relatively near to us, not farther than fifty light-years. There are about 300 stars within that distance. For most of the other stars the displacement is much too small to be seen. Fortunately, there are a number of other more indirect ways to find out about the distance of stars. We shall not here get into the details of these methods. Altogether these measurements have borne out our hypothesis: The stars don't differ much in their actual brightness; if they were all at the same distance, they would

---

[4] Instead of writing big numbers with many zeros, we shall use in this book the common scientific notation with the so-called "powers of ten." 10^{14} means ten to the fourteenth power, that is, 10 times 10 times 10 and so on, fourteen times—thus a number with a one as the first digit and fourteen zeros following it. A million, for example, is written as 10^6.

When we say that Sirius is 10^{14} kilometers away, we do not mean that its distance is exactly this number of kilometers. We only have given the "order of magnitude." It might be $\frac{2}{3}$ of 10^{14} of $1\frac{1}{2}$ times more. For special scientific purposes it is necessary to know this distance much better—it is actually known with very good accuracy—but for our survey it is not necessary to know this figure exactly. It makes no difference for our general insight into the dimensions of the universe whether Sirius is $\frac{1}{2} \times 10^{14}$ kilometers away or 2×10^{14} kilometers. We are interested in the order of magnitude of the expanses of space.

look about equally bright. There are many exceptions to this rule, but it can be used to get a first orientation in regard to the distribution of stars. Actually the rule is much better fulfilled if one compares only stars of similar color. For example, stars that are similar to the Sun (yellowish-white color[5]) will never differ by much: one may be three times as luminous as the other, or a third as strong; these are small differences for our purposes. We make no great error in the distance by assuming them all equally luminous. We should get the right order of magnitude of the distance, and that is all we need in order to get a general idea of the vast distances of the universe.

THE DISTRIBUTION OF THE STARS

Let us look at the sky and form a picture of the stars in space. We see bright ones and faint ones, many more faint stars than bright stars. At first sight it seems that there is no regularity in the distribution of the stars in the sky. But when we look more systematically, using a pair of field glasses on a solid rest, we notice quite clearly that the fainter stars are by no means evenly distributed over the sky. There are many more faint stars in or near the Milky Way, compared with the regions away from it. When we look with good field glasses in a direction far from the Milky Way, we find a few brighter stars but almost no very faint ones. In the Milky Way, however, the background is glittering with millions of stars.

What does this mean? It tells us that the stars are not distributed uniformly in space, but are concentrated in a flat disk. Our solar system is somewhere in that disk. When we look into the body of the disk, we see many stars and many far away ones which appear faint; when we look perpendicular to the plane of the disk, we see only a few stars and, because of their proximity, those relatively bright.

How vast is this disk that contains all the stars we can see in the sky? We again can use our hypothesis and measure the apparent brightness of the faintest stars we see when we look in the direction of the disk (the Milky Way) and when we look out of the plane of the disk. For this we need powerful telescopes that can distinguish

[5] The color the Sun would appear to be when viewed from a very great distance can easily be seen when looking at some of the artificial satellites. They are made of reflecting metal and therefore appear the same color as the Sun.

every single star in the Milky Way. We then can apply our simple
method of determining the distances. Here is the result: The faintest
stars we see when looking into the disk are about 100 times fainter
than those we see when looking out of the disk. Hence the radius of
the disk must be about ten times larger[6] than its thickness. The faintest stars in the Milky Way are about a hundred million times weaker
than Sirius; so they must be 10,000 times farther away than Sirius, or
about a hundred thousand light-years. (See Figure 5.)

The spreading of the stars over the sky, faint and bright, has taught
us that the stars form a circular disk with a diameter of 10^5 light-
years and a thickness of 10^4 light-years. The Sun and the Earth are

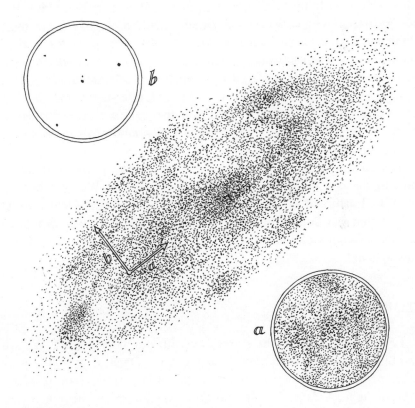

Figure 5.   Sketch of the galaxy with an indication of the position of the sun and
the directions of view in a and b. (a) Stars seen in a telescope looking into the
galaxy. (b) Stars seen looking out of the galaxy.

[6] A light source you will recall, seems 100 times weaker when it is 10 times away.
In general, if it seems x times weaker, it is $\sqrt{x}$ times farther away.

halfway out from the center. This flat colony of stars is called a galactic system; it is our own galaxy. The average distance between the stars in this system is of the order of about ten light-years. This is the distance between the Sun and the nearest stars around us, and seems to be the normal distance between neighbors in our galaxy. From this we can figure out roughly how many stars there are in our galaxy. We get something of the order of fifty billions.

Nowadays we know considerably more about the structure of our galaxy. It contains not only stars but also gases and dust, especially in the center. This interstellar matter causes difficulties when we apply our simple method of measuring distances. When seen through regions of dust and gas, the stars appear fainter, and we might conclude erroneously that they are farther away than they really are. But the astronomers have worked out many methods to overcome these difficulties. Modern radio astronomy, for example, provides a good method to determine where the interstellar gas is located; this gas emits certain definite radio waves which are characteristic of the atom of hydrogen, the principal element of interstellar gas. By this and other methods we have found that the stars are concentrated in great streamers that form large spiral arms, wound around the center in the plane of the disk.

The colony of stars forming our galactic system is the next larger unit in the cosmic environment in which we live. We first considered the Earth and then the solar system as our abode. Now we recognize that the Sun, with its planets, is but a small part of a large assembly—many billions of stars—within our galaxy. What is outside this system?

OTHER GALAXIES

Let us again look at the starry sky with our field glasses. We see the billions of stars contained in our galaxy. Once in a while, however, we see something that is not a star; it is a nebula, an extended area of light. A famous and beautiful example is the nebula in the constellation of Orion. This and many other nebulae have been recognized to be big luminous gas clouds. But there are other nebulae—the most striking is the Andromeda nebula—which in small instruments appear as disk-shaped luminous areas. When these objects are

Plate 1. Andromeda Nebula.

Figure 6.   Jodrell Bank, a modern radio-astronomical instrument.

examined with very strong telescopes, one finds that they consist of a very large number of extremely faint stars, arranged in the same disk-shaped spiral array as our own galaxy. That was a tremendous discovery! Our own galactic system is not the only one. There exist other similar star systems. The number of these galactic objects is quite large. The more powerful the telescope, the more of these galaxies can be seen. They seem to extend deep into space. How far away are they and how are they distributed?

Again we can get an idea of the distance from the apparent brightness of these objects. Let us look at the Andromeda Nebula. (See Plate I.) Its total brightness is roughly equal to that of an average star among those about ten light-years away. Very powerful telescopes show that the number of stars in this unit is of a magnitude similar to our own galaxy, about fifty billions. Therefore we must conclude that the nebula actually is fifty billion times brighter than one of our neighbor stars. It appears equally bright; hence its distance must be $\sqrt{50}$ billions greater than the distance of the nearby stars, or ten light-years times $\sqrt{50}$ billions, which gives about two million light-years. This number has been checked with other more accurate methods and is roughly correct. The distance between our galaxy and the next one is about twenty times the diameter of our galaxy. The light we see coming from the Andromeda Nebula left its source at a time when man had not evolved from his apelike forefathers.

The same method can be applied to the other galaxies we see in the sky: We compare the apparent brightness with the brightness of the Andromeda galaxy and find it, say, X times weaker; we then conclude that the particular galaxy is about $\sqrt{X}$ times farther away. Such a conclusion is based upon the assumption that all galaxies are very roughly equal in size and in actual brightness. There are many detailed observations confirming this assumption.

In this way we can get an idea of the distribution of the many spiral nebulae which are visible with powerful telescopes. There are many millions of them known today. We find that they are rather evenly distributed in all directions, with an average distance between neighboring ones of a few million light-years. The distance between our galaxy and the Andromeda Nebula is about equal to the average distance between galaxies in general. The farther we look, the more galaxies we find. Will this search ever reach an end?

THE EXPANDING UNIVERSE

This question can be answered positively because of a most interesting and unexpected phenomenon which was detected a few decades ago. All these galaxies are moving away from us, and the farther away, the faster they move. How do we know?

We must take a closer look at the light that comes from these nebulae. It is the combined light of all the fifty billion stars that make up a galaxy. A light ray is an electromagnetic wave, as we shall see in Chapter Three, and the frequency of the wave (that is, the number of complete ups and downs the wave goes through each second) determines the color. We can spread light out into a spectrum by passing it through a prism, and we find the colors arranged according to their frequencies: the lower frequencies on one side, the higher on the other. Now we know from studying starlight that, while all the colors seem to be present, certain frequencies are missing. When we look at the spectra of most stars, we do find certain frequencies missing. These absent frequencies are the frequencies of the kind of light that is absorbed by the cool gases on the surface of the stars. We find dark lines in the spectrum just at the places where light of these frequencies would be found had there not been any absorption. For example, most of the star spectra have two dark lines in the violet part of the spectrum, indicating the absorption of calcium gas. We are not astonished to find the same two dark lines in the spectra of distant galaxies, since their light is just the sum of the light of all their stars. But it is, or was, startling that these same two dark lines should be found not at the expected frequency, but shifted toward lower frequencies. In very faint galaxies this shift is so large that the spots are seen at the red end of the spectrum instead of the violet one.

Such frequency shifts are well known and can be directly interpreted as a consequence of the motion of the object relative to the observer. When a light source moves away from the observer, the frequency of the emitted light appears to become lower, just as the pitch of the horn of an automobile sounds lower if the car moves away from us. The shift is proportional to the speed and, hence, can be used to determine the speed of the object moving away from us.

Thus the observed frequency shift of the light of distant galaxies must be interpreted as a proof of the fact that these galaxies are moving away from us. The speed of this motion has turned out to be proportional to the distance. For the nearby galaxies, such as the Andromeda Nebula, the motion is all but unobservable, but galaxies at a distance of about 100 million light-years rush away with the speed of roughly 3000 kilometers per second. The speed in kilometers per second has been found to be always about thirty times the distance in million light-years. This relation between speed and distance was first discovered by the American astronomer Edwin P. Hubble in 1929. At present our largest telescopes can detect galaxies as far away as three billion light-years. They move away from us with a speed of 90,000 kilometers per second, which is almost a third the speed of light.

The expanding motion of the universe of galaxies gives us an indication of the limit of what we can ever see. We might be able to build larger telescopes and try to see galaxies that are still farther away, but they will recede from us with speeds that are nearer and nearer the speed of light. When an object moves away from us with a speed near the speed of light, its radiation will appear to be weakened; in fact, the nearer its speed gets to the speed of light the more the object will fade out, the less visible it will be.

The reason for this is easily understood if you compare the light emitted from a source with bullets shot by a gun in all directions. Obviously the number of hits will be few and weak from a gun receding from us with a speed almost equal to the speed of the projectiles.[7]

Hence even if there are many more galaxies farther than about 10 billion light-years away (the distance at which the Hubble relation would give a receding speed equal to that of light), even if there are an infinite number of them, we cannot see them; they are moving away from us so fast that their light cannot reach us any more.

A universe of expanding distances between galaxies confronts us with an interesting situation: There might well be an infinite number of galaxies spread over infinite distances. But we can see only the ones that recede from us with velocities reasonably below the speed of light. Hence there is only a finite number of them from which light can reach us. Although this universe might actually be infinite, it is finite as far as we are concerned. We can explore only that part of it which can send us its light signals.

It is remarkable that the astronomical instruments at our disposition today, such as the Mount Palomar telescope (Figure 7), already can penetrate into distances at which the speed or recession is one third of the speed of light. This is not very much less than the farthest distance we ever will be able to see. If we can penetrate only about three times farther into space, we essentially will have spanned the visible universe. Therefore we are witnessing today a great moment in the development of mankind, comparable to the achievement of Magellan's first voyage around the globe in 1520. At that time the planet Earth was encompassed and the limits of travel on earth clearly recognized. Today we begin to encompass the limits of penetration into space. We may be beginning to observe the last objects that can be observed.

[7] This example might lead one to the erroneous conclusion that the light emitted backward from a source moving away travels at a speed slower than it would if emitted by a stationary source. Obviously bullets fired from a receding gun would come to us at a slower speed than bullets from a fixed gun.

Light always travels at the same speed (300,000 kilometers per second) whether emitted by a fixed or by a moving source. The behavior of light is governed by the laws of relativity, a theory not discussed in this book. The conclusions drawn from our example are still valid however: the light emitted backward by a moving source is weaker not in its speed, but in its intensity. The backward intensity vanishes if the source itself attains the speed of light.

Figure 7. Mount Palomar Observatory.

LADDER OF DISTANCES

Let us now summarize the sizes of things as we have developed them. We build up a ladder of distances step by step, starting with the smallest distance we can perceive with our naked eyes and ascending to the stars.

The smallest distance we can distinguish is about one tenth of a millimeter. It is the width of a hair. The next step on our ladder is a distance characteristic of our own size—the distance from our eye to the tip of our arm; ten thousand times larger than the first one, it is about one meter. The distance to the mountains plainly visible at the horizon is again ten thousand times more: ten kilometers. The diameter of the Earth is the next step; it is about 1000 times more, namely 12,000 kilometers. The distance Earth-Sun is again about 10,000 times larger; it is 150 million kilometers. The next step of our distance ladder is the distance to the nearest stars; this time the jump is a factor one million, and we get 10^{14} kilometers, or ten light-years. The following step is the size of our galaxy, which is again 10,000 times the previous distance, namely 10^5 light-years. The next step is larger only by a factor between 10 and 100; it leads us to the distance between nearest galaxies, which is several million light-years. The final step, another factor 10,000, brings us to the distance of the farthest objects which ever can be seen, to what we may call the radius of the accessible universe: according to today's best knowledge, it is something of the order of ten billion light-years.

This is the end of our ladder of distances. Each step has led to a greater distance. In most cases the increase was by a factor of ten thousand. Such a step is easily within our ability and can be visualized by remembering that the length of our arm is about 10,000 times the width of hair, or that a distance of ten miles is removed by the same factor from the length of our own body. Even the factor one million, which occurs between the distance Earth-Sun and the distance to the next star, can be comprehended: the distance to Sirius is to the distance to the Sun as 100 yards is to a hair's breadth. Our intuition begins to falter, however, when we try to grasp the extension of the whole ladder. The tremendous expanses of the visible universe are too great for any immediate comprehension in terms of terrestrial sizes. All the greater is the achievement of the human mind, wherein were created the ideas which have led to the recognition of the vast dimensions of the universe. Blaise Pascal, the great French philosopher, said, "It is not the vastness of the field of stars which deserves our admiration, it is man who has measured it."

DISTANCE LADDER

Distance		*Ratio between steps*
Smallest visible distance	0.1 mm.	
		10,000
Human dimensions	1 m.	
		10,000
Objects in landscape	10 km.	
		1000
Diameter of Earth	1.2×10^4 km.	
		10,000
Earth-Sun	1.5×10^8 km.	
		1,000,000
Sun-Sirius	10^{14} km.	
		10,000
Size of galaxy	10^{18} km.	
		10
Distance of near galaxy	10^{19} km.	
		10,000
Size of universe	10^{23} km.	

OUR PLACE IN TIME

Chapter Two

THE AGE OF THE LANDSCAPE

How old is the world? We have an immediate perception of time intervals pertaining to our life. The shortest time that we can sense directly is about a tenth of a second. It is the duration of a snap of a finger. The natural units of time we deal with in our daily life are the day and the year, and we know what it means when we speak of a man's life span. Recorded history traces back the flow of time for about 5000 years. This takes us back to the Sumerian civilization, which is the most ancient period known to us from written records. Hence 5000 years is the longest period of which we have direct human experience. If we want to learn the chronology of events that antecede human history, we must use indirect methods.

The large forms of nature around us—mountains, hills, rivers, oceans, plains, etc.—have not changed much in the course of written history. Have they been here for eternity? Evidently not. Wind and weather are wearing them down.

Let us consider a mountain such as the Matterhorn, which is in the Alps between Italy and Switzerland. It rises above its immediate surroundings about 2000 meters and, at its base, is about 2000 meters broad. Hence it contains roughly 2×10^9 cubic meters of rock. Its slopes have an area of roughly 10^7 square meters. The weather— rain, ice, and storm—breaks off little pieces of rock here and there, mainly by freezing water in cracks, and the mighty structure is slowly destroyed. How long would it take to level it down? Let us perform a simple calculation. It is reasonable to assume that on the average a piece of rock a few inches in size is broken off per year from every square meter. This gives us about 10^3 cubic meters per year coming down from the Matterhorn. After a million years half of the mountain would be gone. The life of a mountain such as the Matterhorn must be of the order of millions of years.

We come to similar conclusions when we study the amount of material the rivers transport to the seas. We can measure the amount of fine-grained rock, sand, and soil swept from the land by rain and brought to the sea by the rivers in one year. If this material were distributed evenly over the land from which the rivers come, it would be a very thin layer, only 1/300 of a centimeter thick. In a million years, however, it would be a layer of thirty meters. Since the material does not come evenly from all points, but only from spots where there is a slope, we see that rain and weather in one million years can remove hills many hundred meters high and change our landscape appreciably. So the age of the landscape we see around us can be counted in millions of years.

Erosion by rain and wind is the destructive leveling force that has shaped the surface of the earth. If there were no other force acting, the world would all be flat, since mountains and hills would have been erased in a few million years. But there are constructive forces at work that slowly but constantly change the surface of the earth. The inside of the earth is under high pressure, since it sustains the whole weight of the outer layers. This pressure sometimes is released at one point, or increases at another. (See Figure 8.) The pressure changes cause movements of the surface, up and down; high pla-

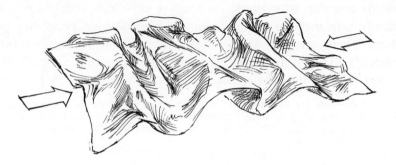

Figure 8. Surface of Earth like piece of cloth.

teaus are formed and deep depressions. Sometimes the movements are sideways, and the surface curls up to form ridges and valleys, just as a piece of cloth does when it is pushed inward from two opposite sides. There is a constant interplay of mountain formation and subsequent destruction by erosion. We live in a period separated by only a few million years from a time of very violent mountain formations; this is why the surface of the earth now exhibits so many different mountain ranges. Some fifty million years from now the earth might be much flatter and less interesting, if no new mountain-forming event should occur in the meantime.

RADIOACTIVITY, THE CLOCK OF THE UNIVERSE

How long did this constant interplay between mountain formation and atmospheric mountain destruction go on? How can we measure the time intervals in which the great geological events occurred? We must use a natural clock which turns slowly enough to measure long times in a way we can read. Fortunately, Nature has provided a very slow, regular process which can be used for time measurements. It is radioactivity, the strange phenomenon discovered in 1896 by the Frenchman Henri Becquerel. But how can radioactivity be used as a clock?

When it was discovered, radioactivity puzzled everyone because it disproved the old belief that chemical elements[1] are unchangeable. The phenomenon of radioactivity shows that some elements are not. A radioactive substance changes over into another substance. The atoms of such a substance undergo a decay with the emission of rays and become the atoms of another element.

Let us consider an example, radioactive rubidium. Rubidium is a relatively rare metallic element, somewhat similar to potassium or sodium. There are two kinds of rubidium found in nature (two "isotopes"). They differ in weight; one has the atomic weight[2] 85, the other 87, and the heavier one is a radioactive element. A piece of

---

[1] Chemical elements are the materials of which all forms of matter are composed, such as iron, gold, oxygen, sulfur, carbon, etc. We will learn much more about elements in Chapter Three. The phenomenon of radioactivity is discussed in more detail in Chapter Seven.

[2] The atomic weight is the weight of an atom compared to the weight of the lightest atom, the hydrogen atom. Rubidium 85 has an atom that weighs 85 times as much as the hydrogen atom.

pure Rb^{87} emits a characteristic radiation whose nature is not important to us here. (It is quite important to the medical profession, since it can be used in the treatment of cancer.) The main point is the fact that one atom of Rb^{87} changes into a different kind of atom, into an atom of strontium. This transformation occurs slowly and steadily at a fixed rate in time which cannot be accelerated or slowed down by any outside influence. Every year a certain fraction of Rb^{87} is transformed into strontium. For Rb this fraction is extremely small; it is only 1.6×10^{-11} per year.[3] This means that every year a hundredth of a billionth of Rb^{87} changes into strontium. Most of the radioactive substances found in nature transform as slowly as this. The "decay constant" of uranium is 2×10^{-10} per year, which means that only two parts in ten billions (10^{10}) change every year. Potassium 40, also a radioactive element, has a decay constant of 0.7×10^{-9} per year.

Our knowledge of radioactivity has increased greatly since the invention of high energy accelerators (atom smashers). In these machines small particles are hurled with high energies against the atoms of various substances, and they produce changes in those atoms. For example, normally non-radioactive elements are changed under bombardment in these machines into new elements which in most cases are not found in nature and very often are radioactive. Thus one can produce new "artificial" man-made radioactive materials of great value in physical and medical research. Most of them transform very much faster than the natural radioactive elements. For example, one can produce a radioactive sodium (weight 24) which transforms into magnesium at the rate of 6 per cent per hour.

THE AGE OF MATTER

Now we come to our first fundamental conclusion about cosmic time scales: The earth could not have existed forever. There are things on Earth that could not have been here forever. If the Earth had existed for an infinite time, we could not find naturally radioactive substances on its surface, such as Rb^{87}, uranium, and potassium. In fact, if the age of the Earth were much greater than

[3] Here we use the method of negative powers of ten in order to express very small numbers. 10^{-1} means $1/10$; 10^{-2} means $1/10 \times 1/10 = 1/100$; 10^{-11} means $1/10 \times 1/10 \times \ldots$ eleven times. One can also say that $10^{-11} = 0.00 \ldots 1$ with eleven zeros, including the first zero before the decimal point.

10^{10} years, all the naturally occurring radioactive substances we have mentioned would have transformed almost completely into their daughter products and would not be found. We must assume that the process that made those elements no longer continues.

How old, then, is the Earth? When we look at the decay constants of the radioactive substances found in nature, we observe that the decay constants are always less than one billionth per year. The artificial radioactive materials, however, the elements which we produce ourselves, have all kinds of decay constants. They range from slow decays, such as a fraction of a millionth per year, to really fast decays, such as the decay of half the material in a few tenths of a second. Examples of all decay speeds between these limits have been found. But only those decaying more slowly than a billionth in a year are ever seen occurring in nature. The explanation is quite simple. The faster ones cannot be found since they already have disappeared in the time the Earth has existed.[4]

From this we conclude that the matter of the Earth must have existed in its present state for several billion years but not much longer. The naturally radioactive element with the fastest decay is potassium (K^{40}) (one billionth per year) and already it is all but gone; it is found only as a very small percentage (0.12 per cent) of ordinary potassium. The "age" of the matter which composes our Earth must therefore be somewhat longer than one billion years, perhaps five or ten times longer, but not much more.

It was an impressive moment in the history of our scientific recognition of the world when proof was found, here on Earth, that the Earth had not existed forever. The radioactive materials are only a tiny part of the Earth. They are extremely rare. Still their very existence bears witness of a beginning of some sort.

What happened at that beginning? Evidently the Earth could not have been in a state resembling the present situation. At that time the material of which the Earth is made must have been subject to conditions under which radioactive elements could have been created. These are the conditions that we produce in our big nuclear ac-

---

[4] There are interesting exceptions, which show how easily a false clue can fool one. In fact there exist a few fast-decaying radioactive elements in nature. However, they are all what we call "daughter substances" of slowly decaying radioactive elements. Here is what this means. It happens sometimes that the product of a radioactive decay is again radioactive and also decays into a third element. Such a product is called a "daughter substance." If the first decay is very slow, and the second is fast, we observe the fast decay in nature every time following the slow one.

celerators. Particles and atoms must have been moving with tremendous energies and at high densities, colliding with each other at great speed. The temperatures necessary to produce these conditions range in the region of 100 million degrees. We have good reasons to believe that such conditions occur in the center of stars, not in ordinary circumstances, but when stars become unstable and explode. Exploding stars are called novae, because they appear suddenly as new stars in the sky and fade away in a few months. They are nothing very unusual. With our giant telescopes we can find twenty or thirty per year among the fifty billion stars of a galaxy.[5]

Hence we come to the conclusion that the material of which the Earth is made must have been subjected to tremendous heat and acceleration, probably in exploding stars, at a time which lies roughly five to ten billion years in the past. We can consider these events as the creation of the elements of which our environment is made.[6] At that time many radioactive and non-radioactive elements were created, including all those we can make with our nuclear machines and certainly a few more. But the radioactive substances with shorter lifetimes have long since decayed and are transformed into stable elements. The few long-lived, naturally radioactive substances are the last witnesses of the eventful times at which the elements were formed—the elements which now make up matter on Earth. They are the last embers still remaining from the great cosmic fire which, ten billion years ago, created the materials we see around us on Earth.

THE DATING OF EVENTS IN THE EARTH'S HISTORY

A closer analysis of the decay process of natural radioactivity allows us to determine other events more recent than the birth of our elements. A mineral containing a naturally radioactive product contains also the decay product of radioactivity in most cases. For example, in a rock containing rubidium, one also finds strontium, the element into which the radioactive rubidium transforms. By comparing the relative amounts of the two elements, one can calculate how long the rubidium was kept in this rock, or, in other words,

[5] The chances that an ordinary star such as the Sun will explode are not very high. It happens only once in a few billion years. The last explosion in our neighborhood (within 1000 light-years) happened in 1750.
[6] Chapter Nine contains a discussion of element formation in stars.

one can calculate the time that has elapsed since that piece of rock solidified. The calculation is quite simple. Every year 1.6×10^{-11} part of the rubidium turns into strontium, and one can infer therefore how many years it took to get the observed amount of strontium.

There is only one hitch in it. Not all the strontium in the rock need have been rubidium before. The rock might have picked up original strontium too. There is a very elegant method to avoid this difficulty. The strontium from rubidium is a very special one, namely Sr^{87}. Normal strontium consists only of 12 per cent Sr^{87} and the bulk is another strontium isotope, Sr^{88}.[7] Hence all one has to do is to measure also the amount of Sr^{88} in the rock. If none is found, then all Sr^{87} must have come from radioactive rubidium. If there is some, then we know how much ordinary strontium was mixed into the rock, and we can determine how much Sr^{87} was added by radioactive decay.

Similar measurements can be made with rocks containing any other natural radioactivity. The radioactivity of potassium and uranium have been used widely for this purpose.

The naturally radioactive materials do more than bear witness of the origin of the Earth; they also can be used as time markers when they slowly tick away with their regular decay.

The measurement of the radioactive-decay products such as strontium from rubidium has made it possible to determine the time of events which happened in the gap between the million years of erosion of our landscape and the many billion years ago when our elements were formed. Whenever new mountain ranges appeared, whenever the seas deposited sediment on their floors, the radioactive elements contained in the material began to accumulate their decay products, and we can time the event by measuring the amounts of accumulation. We then obtain a reasonably accurate timetable of geological events. We find, for example, that the Alps and the Himalayan mountain ranges are quite young, only a few million years old. (See Figure 9.) The Rocky Mountains in their present form are older, about 60–100 million years. The flat ridges of the Appalachian range are as old as 250 to 300 million years, although the actual shapes of the hills at the surface have changed many times since then.

[7] The symbol Sr^{87} or Sr^{88} means a strontium whose atoms weigh 87 or 88 times the weight of a hydrogen atom, respectively. The number 87 or 88 is the atomic weight of strontium.

Figure 9. K2 in the Himalayas (28,250 feet) considered the second highest peak in the world.

The oldest rocks found so far have an age of 2.6 billion years. Hence the age of the Earth must be at least as great. The Earth is probably older than this, but what is now the surface of the planet has changed so much that no rock is found today that could show greater age.

The different layers of rocks and sediment include fossils of animals and plants. So the timetable of geological formations leads directly to a timetable of the development of life. (See Figure 10.) We find that the earliest records of life start about 600 million years ago with fossils of algae and sponges. Evidently there must have been life earlier in a more primitive form that has left no record in rocks. It is estimated that primitive bacteria must have existed for a billion or more years. Fish and snails of some 300 million years ago are found; reptiles began to exist about 275 million years ago. The latter

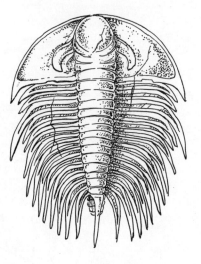

Figure 10.   Trilobite (Olenellus), Cambrian Period.

awaited the development of trees and flowers which first appeared 400 million years ago. Mammals developed only 150 million years ago, and man has existed barely a million years. Thus the radioactive clocks have helped also to date the development of life.

THE AGE OF THE EARTH AND THE PLANETS

Now and then a piece of matter enters our atmosphere from outer space. Most of these objects—they are called meteorites—evaporate when they enter the atmosphere, because of the intense heat created as they speed through the air. Some larger chunks, however, do reach the surface of the Earth intact (See Figure 11). These objects and the paths that led them to us have been studied. It is probable that the meteorites do not come from very far. They are possibly the broken remnants of one or several small planets which disintegrated sometime at the beginning of the history of the solar system. The age of these rocks must be close to the age of the solar system itself; they probably date from the time when matter assembled in the form of the Sun and the planets. Hence when we can determine the age of these fragments, we probably have measured the age of our solar system, or the time when the planets were formed. Fortunately, the meteorites sometimes contain traces of a radioactive material and its decay products. The amount of the decay product can be used to determine how long the radioactive material decayed inside the piece of matter from outer space. The result has been very consistent: all meteorites seem to be of the same age, an age of 4.5 billion years. We must conclude that this time has passed since matter accumulated into planets in our solar system. Very probably this is also the time our Earth and the other planets have existed as big globes circling the Sun.

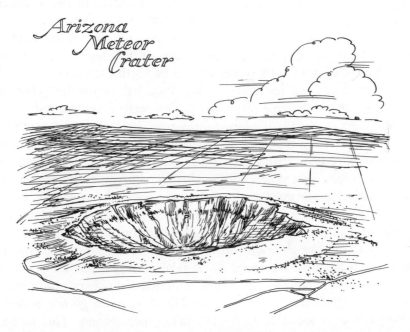

Figure 11. Arizona Meteor Crater. Probably fell some tens of thousands of years ago. About 1360 yards in diameter and about 650 feet deep. Probably blasted by a tremendous meteor of iron and nickel which is probably 400 feet below the floor of the crater and over to one side.

THE AGE OF THE STARS

Can we determine the age of other stars? We no longer can use the radioactive clock, since no material reaches us from outside the solar system. Our only means of communication is the light. Still, in spite of the lack of any direct contact, astronomers have tried to get some indirect information about the age of stars. Sometimes it is possible to come to some tentative conclusions by investigating carefully the color and the brightness of stars and by using our new ideas about the processes that produce all the immense energy required to keep a star shining and hot for long periods.[8] From such arguments one finds that the life spans of most stars are measured also in billions of years. Some star groups are possibly as old as twenty or thirty billion years; others may be younger.

Just as the year is a suitable unit for the measure of human life, a billion years is the suitable unit for the life of stars. The oldest rocks on Earth are 2.6 billion years old; the solar system must have been formed 4.5 billion years ago; our naturally radioactive substances were formed in some star explosion five or ten billion years ago, and the age of most stars seems also to lie in this interval.

The expansion of the universe we discussed in the last chapter also gives us a time scale on which the universe develops: today we see the galaxies steadily streaming away from us, the faster the farther away they are. We then can ask the question: If it is true that the galaxies move apart from each other, must not there have been a time when they were nearer to one another? In fact, if the expansion of the universe has gone on at the same rate as it goes now, there must have been a time when all galaxies were crowded close together at the same place. Hence the expansion of the galaxies we see could not have gone on forever. When was that time of crowding? We recall that the speed of a galaxy away from us is about thirty kilometers per second for every million light-years of distance. It is most significant that it takes ten billion years to go one million light-years at a speed of thirty kilometers per second. This means that the expansion of the galaxies could not have gone on at the same rate for longer than ten billion years. Tracing the expansion backward, we must conclude that at that time all galaxies would have been concentrated roughly at the same place.

Again we find a time similar to the other cosmic lifetimes. What is the meaning for us? Not much more than this: The visible universe of ten billion years ago and the matter it contained must have been very different from what it is now. The world as we know it here and now, with its matter, its stars and planets, its galaxies and system of galaxies, has existed for tens of millions of years. Nobody knows

[8] See Chapter Five about this.

today in what state the world may earlier have been. Matter, stars, and galaxies come and go. All we know today is that the process takes roughly ten billion years.

TIME LADDER

Shortest time interval distinguishable by ear	0.1 seconds
Day	10^5 seconds
Human life	10^9 seconds$=100$ years
Human civilization	10^4 years
Development of man	
Significant change of Earth surface	10^6 years
Development of mammals	
Age of Rocky Mountains	10^8 years
Development of life	
Age of many rocks	2×10^9 years
Age of Earth	4.5×10^9
Age of matter our nearest stars (including Sun, Earth) are made of	$5-10\times10^9$
Age of universe	$10-20\times10^9$ years

If the age of the universe is taken as one day, mankind has existed only for the last ten seconds.

TWO FORCES OF NATURE

Chapter Three

In Chapters One and Two we have set the stage in time and space for what goes on in nature. We now turn our attention to the events on this stage. Here we find an overwhelming multitude of objects, in constant change and motion in the sky and on Earth, with varying properties and qualities ranging all the way from simple gases, liquids, solids to such intricate aggregates as plants, animals, and men. The behavior of all forms of matter is highly complicated and bewildering. Still we can perceive some kind of order in nature. In spite of constant change and movement, we recognize similarities between different objects; we range them into classes and we have names for them. The materials of which they are made can be classified into definite types, such as rocks, metals, liquids, organic substances, etc. These substances differ widely in their properties, but we observe everywhere the same kinds of metals, the same kinds of rock, the same kinds of organic material and so forth. A piece of gold is the same wherever on Earth it is found. In the living world too, we recognize similarities and identities. They are strikingly embodied in what we call the different species; we find bacteria, trees, flowers, animals that have common properties and are identifiable as being of the same kind.

These are the regularities we want to understand. We want to know why nature has specific forms, why the forms are such and not otherwise, and why the objects behave as we see them behave. To begin with, however, we must first look for simple features in nature which are unspecific and common to all objects. This chapter is devoted to two of these features. One is the phenomenon of gravity and the other is light.

GRAVITY ON EARTH AND IN THE SKY

Gravity is a well-known phenomenon here on Earth. All things around us, large or small, are attracted by the Earth—they fall downward when they are not held up by some support. The attraction of every piece of matter by the Earth is the best-known example of a force in nature. Still, it needed a tremendous effort and centuries of thinking before mankind recognized that the motion of the Moon around the Earth and of the planets around the Sun is based upon the same force. It long was thought that the laws governing heavenly bodies were different from those that held on Earth. The universality of the laws of nature, their validity for the whole universe, has been recognized only since the days of Isaac Newton.

The Moon and the planets do not fall toward the Earth nor toward the Sun; how then could their motion be governed by the force of gravity? There is a big gap between our terrestrial experience of things falling toward the Earth and the heavenly appearance of bodies orbiting around a center (Moon around Earth, planets around Sun). The bridging of this gap was a decisive step toward the understanding of the universe. Let us see how it came about.

Imagine that we are at the top of a very high tower and throw a stone horizontally into space. (See Figure 12.) The stone's path will be bent down toward the Earth because of gravity, and the stone will hit the ground at a certain distance away from the tower. The harder we throw the stone, the more gradual will be the bending of the path. We can imagine that the stone could be thrown with such vigor that the downward bend of its path would just equal the curvature of the Earth's surface, which is, of course, the surface of a sphere. Then the stone would never reach the surface because whenever its path bent down, the surface of the Earth would bend by the same amount. We have thrown the stone, as it were, beyond the horizon. If the air did not slow it down, our stone would circle the Earth as a satellite. This is, of course, the principle of launching a rocket satellite. In a

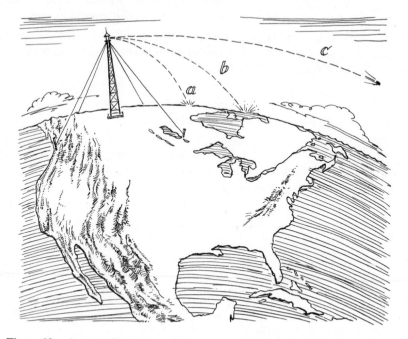

Figure 12. A stone thrown from a tower. The paths a, b, c correspond to throwings of increasing power. The throw c will never reach the earth.

typical rocket firing, the first stage raises the satellite above the atmosphere, and then a second rocket explosion pushes it into a horizontal motion. The horizontal speed necessary for the bending to be equal to the Earth's curvature is about five miles per second. Thus we see how the falling motion of an object can go over into an orbiting motion around the Earth if the object receives a strong horizontal push.

Let us now look at the orbit of a body around a center of attraction in a different way. When the planet circles the Sun, the attractive force of gravity keeps the orbit circular, just as a weight tied to the end of a string keeps moving on a circle if you whirl it around while holding the other end of the string. The attractive force counteracts the centrifugal force, which in a circular motion pushes things outward.

The centrifugal force (the drag on the string) is the greater the more rounds the object makes per second. It is also greater for larger radii, and it is, of course, proportional to the mass of the object. In fact, we can easily calculate the centrifugal force on each planet, since we know its revolution time and its distance from the Sun.

The centrifugal force is just balanced by the attractive force of gravity; hence whenever we calculate a centrifugal force in an orbit, we have determined the force of gravity. That is the way Newton measured the force of gravity of the Sun upon the planets and of the planets upon their moons. He found that gravity follows a very simple law: The attraction between two bodies is proportional to the product of the masses and inversely proportional to the square of their distance. For example, the distance of Venus from the Sun is 0.7 times the distance of the Earth from the Sun. In order to keep Venus on its orbit with the observed revolution time, the attraction[1] has to be about twice as strong as the Sun's attraction for the Earth. This corresponds to the inverse ratio of the square of the distances, since $(0.7)^2 = \frac{1}{2}$. This calculation is the measurement by human beings of a force far, far beyond direct human experience, a force in our sky.

In order to be sure that the force between the Sun and the planets is a universal force that acts between any two masses, one must show that the same kind of attraction exists between two blocks of lead or any other two objects, and that this force also decreases with the square of the distance and is proportional to the product of the masses. Of course the gravitational force between two lead blocks would be extremely small, since their mass is small compared to that of the heavenly bodies. If the blocks weigh 100 pounds each, the force between them at a distance of one foot is as small as the gravity force which the Earth exerts upon one four-thousandth of a gram. Still, it has been measured, and these measurements do bear out the general validity and universality of the law of gravity.

THE GENERALITY OF THE LAW OF GRAVITY

Newton's discovery of the law of gravity explained for us the orbits of the planets around the Sun. But it also put an end to the old and cherished dream of many philosophers. The dream was to find a fundamental significance in the actual sizes of the orbits and the durations of the periods of the planets. One might have expected

[1] We need not be concerned here about the masses of the Earth and Venus, which happened to be about equal; the mass terms cancel out in the calculation.

that the radii of the planetary orbits would have simple relations; for example, the radius should always be doubled from one planet to the next, or should exhibit some other simple numerical regularity. The Pythagorean philosophers, for instance, attributed special importance to the numerical ratios between heavenly orbits, and they considered them as the essence of their system. These relations were the embodiment of a "harmony of the spheres"; they were supposed to reflect an inherent symmetry of the heavenly world as contrasted to the earthly world, which is full of disorder and without any symmetry. The harmonious interplay of the various celestial motions was supposed to produce a music whose chords were audible to the intellectual ear, a manifestation of the divine order of the universe. Even Johannes Kepler, whose analysis of planetary motions led to the discovery of the law of gravitation, tried hard to explain the observed sizes of the orbits by inventing a universe of regular solids—the sphere, cube, tetrahedron, etc.—one inscribed in the next, and each determining the size of one of the orbits by virtue of some deep, fundamental, all-embracing principle. (See Figure 13.)

With Newton all these ideas turned out to be illusions. The fundamental principle underlying planetary motion is the law of gravitational attraction. It determines the orbits of the planets only insofar as it requires them to be circles or ellipses with the Sun in the center of the circles or in one of the foci of each ellipse, and establishes a special relation between the radius (or major axis of the ellipse) and the period of revolution. But the principle does not prescribe any special size or radius. In fact the actual size of an orbit depends on the conditions at the beginning, when the solar system was formed, and on the subsequent perturbations upon the orbits. For example, if initially the Earth had received a different speed, it would have circled on a larger orbit. Furthermore, if another star should pass near our solar system, all planetary orbits would be changed, and the relations between their sizes and periods would be quite different after the encounter.

We can see from this that the orbit sizes, as observed today, are of no great significance. They could just as well be quite different without violating any law of physics. The fundamental law of gravity determines only the general character of the phenomenon. It admits a continuous variety of realizations. The actual orbits depend on influences that acted before the phenomenon developed without fur-

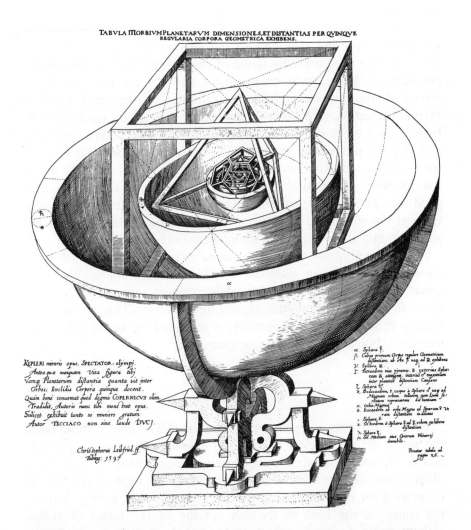

Figure 13. Kepler Device. Kepler's model of the Universe showing how he thought all the planets were positioned with relation to certain geometric shapes. From MYSTERIUM COSMOGRAPHICUM (1597, edition of 1620) drawn by Christophurus Leibfried.

ther interference from outside. The present orbits can perhaps be traced to some definite causes, such as some special conditions prevailing during the formation of the solar system, or to the influence of passing stars, but there is nothing fundamental in their present magnitudes. We expect the planets of another star to circle on quite different orbits even if the star is very similar to our Sun in its size and constitution.

Because of its universality, the force of gravity reaches beyond the solar system and even beyond our galaxy. The stars within each galaxy attract each other by virtue of gravity, and each galaxy exerts gravitational forces upon other galaxies. Hence the motions of the stars and also the motions of the galaxies are regulated by their mutual attraction. We don't know enough yet about these motions because they are very hard to observe, and we would have to solve a very difficult problem of mathematical analysis if we were to find out what motions an assembly of fifty billion stars would perform under the influence of mutual gravitational attraction. There are very good indications, however, that the same principle governs the motions of the stars. The stars seem to circle around the center of the galaxy in much the same way the planets circle around the Sun.

Are the motions of the galaxies also determined by gravity forces? Here we come to an unsolved problem of astronomy. We don't know much about it except for the striking motion of the galaxies away from each other—the expanding universe. This motion obviously cannot come from gravity; there must be some other fundamental, but as yet unknown, explanation.

LIGHT

Is there anything more universal than light? The light coming from the Sun to the Earth is the basis of our existence. It furnishes warmth and is the source of almost all energy on our planet. It makes the plants grow, and we use the plants as fuel in the form of coal or oil or as food for man and animal. The only sources of energy that do not come via the light of the Sun are the "dark" forces of radioactivity and uranium fission. Last but not least, it is in the bright light of the Sun that Nature appears to us in all her beauty.

Light is our only messenger from the stars, as Galileo said; it must tell us almost everything we shall ever know about the universe. Except for the meager information we get from cosmic rays and meteorites, and whatever we may learn some day from interstellar travel, we have no communication other than by light with the world outside our Earth.

What is light? The answer to this question is found in one of the last century's most interesting developments in physics. Light signals travel through empty space in straight lines with a fixed speed of 3×10^5 kilometers per second. In the time it takes to snap your finger (one tenth of a second) light traverses a distance equal to the trip around the Earth. As we learned in the previous chapter, it takes only minutes for light to travel between the planets and the Sun within our solar system.

When a light signal is sent from one point to another, what is it that goes from the source to the recipient? At first people naturally believed that the light source ejects some light units, impulses or particles, different kinds for different colors. Even the great Newton thought that light consisted of particles (though he cautiously hedged his belief). It was Christian Huygens in Holland who first suggested, in the seventeenth century, that light is a wave motion, and Thomas Young and Augustin Fresnel, at the beginning of the nineteenth century, established beyond doubt that a light beam is a wave traveling through space.

What, we now must ask, is a wave? The most common examples are water waves, but they are not the best illustration for the understanding of light waves because they travel on the surface of the water, whereas light waves go through all space. Still, water waves are instructive for the understanding of wave nature.

A wave moves in a carrier. The surface of the water is the carrier of water waves. The carrier undergoes oscillatory periodic changes: the surface of the water, for example, moves up and down. These changes are so arranged that they move along and make up the characteristic pattern of a traveling wave. We must realize that there is nothing material that travels with the wave. Only the changes of the surface pattern move along as a wave travels. No water is actually transported. Still a wave can transmit effects from one place to another. When I push the surface of water at one side of a vessel in a given direction, the resulting wave transmits this push to the other side of the vessel. Water waves can transmit large amounts of power, as we often witness in the effects of waves at the seashore. But the water itself does not move bodily along with the wave. It only moves up and down, back and forth.

Another example, closer to light, is the sound wave. The carrier of sound is the air. The oscillatory changes which the carrier undergoes are air-pressure changes. When the sound is produced, say, by a loud speaker, the surface of the speaker moves back and forth, thus producing periodic ups and downs in the air pressure near by. These ups and downs move on in all directions, just as waves on a water surface radiate outward when you move your hand back and forth in the water. In the water, however, the wave spreads only over the surface; in the air it spreads in all directions of space. This spread of periodic squeezes and releases is a sound wave. When the oscillation reaches the ear, it transmits the pressure to the ear drum, which is put into the same vibrations the source has performed. This pattern of vibration is perceived as sound. The shorter the distance between the ups and downs, or (which is the same) the more frequently squeezes and releases alternate when the wave arrives at the ear, the higher is the pitch we perceive. The distance between subsequent ups (or downs) is called the wave length, and the number of ups arriving at the ear (or passing by a given point) per second is called the frequency of the wave. The shorter the wave length, the higher the frequency.

Although he did not have many facts to go on, Huygens anticipated this idea of light as a wave motion in 1680. The final recognition of light as a wave occurred to an English scientist who started as a medical man, Thomas Young, born in 1773. He worked on problems of light from 1800 on, and he was the first to find the decisive facts which show that light is a wave motion.

WHY LIGHT IS A WAVE

The vibrations occurring in a light wave cannot be seen directly; only indirect evidence can convince us of the wave nature of light. The best proof today is still the argument Young gave. He based his reasoning upon the phenomenon of "interference." Interference is an effect where, under certain conditions, light added to light gives darkness. The phenomenon shows that light is a wave, since it occurs when a wave crest of one wave coincides with a wave trough of another. Dabble a finger of each hand in water and very closely watch the two waves penetrating each other. You will see that the wave motion is quenched wherever a crest falls upon a trough.

There are many ways to demonstrate the same phenomenon with light waves. One well-known effect is the colored bands and rings you see when a thin film of oil is spread over a surface. The colors are often visible at the edges of a patch of oil on a street pavement. Here light from the sky or from a street light is reflected, first at the upper surface of the oil film and then at the lower surface. The beam of light reflected at the lower surface is behind the beam reflected at the upper surface by a distance of twice the thickness of the film. The two reflected beams "interfere" in the following way: if the thickness of the oil film is a quarter of a wave length, the second is behind the first by half a wave length. The crests of the wave reflected from one surface fall upon the troughs of the wave reflected from the other one, and we get darkness. This interference causes the white daylight to become colored upon reflection; white is a combination of all colors. Certain colors may have just the wave length that gives darkness upon reflection. The reflected light then appears in the hue of the remaining colors.[2]

You can observe this interference effect in a simple experiment. Hold a phonograph record at eye level with a lamp in the background, in such a position that the light from the lamp strikes the flat record at a very small angle. You will see a pattern of color on the record edge near your eye. Light beams reflected from different grooves on the record interfere with one another, causing bands of darkness and bands of bright color.

Another example of interference effects is shown in Figure 14, which illustrates what happens when a sharp edge casts a shadow on a screen. Light waves are scattered at the edge of the barrier, as indicated in Figure 14. Part of the scattered light falls into the

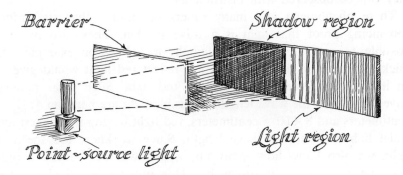

Figure 14. Light and barrier making interference pattern.

[2] It is easy to observe that the apparent colors change when you look at the oil patch at different angles. If the light penetrates the oil film at an angle, the shift between the two reflected beams is different, hence also the color of the non-reflected light.

region of shadows, thereby lighting it up weakly near the edge of the shadow. But the part that is scattered into the region of light interferes with the direct light also arriving in that region. For example, if the detour of the scattered light on its way to point A (see Figure 15) is half a wave length (or three halves, or five halves) longer

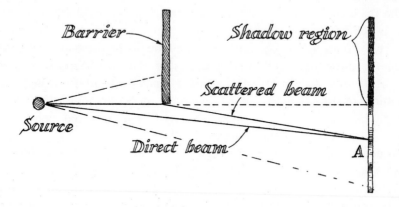

Figure 15. The Interference of Light. When the direct beam is shorter by 1/2, 3/2, 5/2. . . . wave lengths than the scattered beam (source⟶edge of obstacle ⟶A), there will be darkness at A. This is Fig. 14, as seen from above.

than the path of the straight light, the two beams will give darkness. Hence we get a pattern of dark stripes near the edge of the shadow. The smaller the wave length, the narrower the stripes are. Ordinarily these stripes are invisible to the naked eye, but, as shown in Plate II, they can be observed with instruments.

These phenomena and many others of similar character afford convincing proof that light is a wave motion. They also make it possible to measure the wave length of light. For example, the thickness of an oil film that does not reflect red light would give us an indication of the wave length of red light. Such measurements have shown that the wave lengths of visible light are between 4×10^{-5} centimeters and 8×10^{-5} centimeters, red light having the longest and violet light the shortest wave length. Since we know the speed of light, we also know how many ups and downs per second a light wave performs when it rushes by. This number is called the frequency of the light. It gives the number of vibrations in a light wave per second. Red light has a frequency of 4×10^{14} per second, violet light about 8×10^{14} per second. This is a tremendously fast vibration which cannot be directly observed.

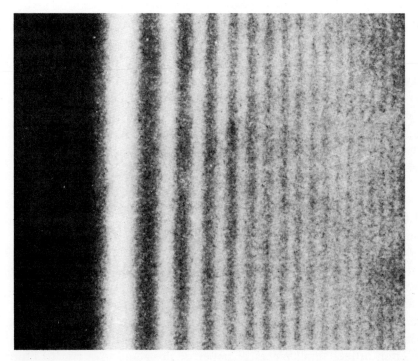

Plate II. An actual photograph of the interference pattern created by light passing a sharp-edged screen.

After we have recognized the wave nature of light, we must face an important question: What kind of waves are light waves? What is the carrier, and what are the oscillatory changes that make up the waves? The answer to this essential question was discovered late in the nineteenth century by James Clerk Maxwell and Heinrich Hertz. The sequence of ideas and discoveries that led to this answer is one of the most exciting developments in science. But before we can give the answer, we must introduce two fundamental phenomena, electricity and magnetism.

ELECTRICITY

A superficial look at natural phenomena does not reveal the pervading importance of electricity. The only obviously electric phenomena in nature seem to be lightning and friction electricity. While the former impresses us with its grandeur and destructiveness, the latter is not impressive at all. Friction electricity is sometimes seen when non-metallic substances, after being rubbed with some material, attract small pieces of paper or dust, and give rise to little electric discharges when brought in contact with metal. These phenomena do not give the impression of being as fundamental as gravity or light and until the end of the eighteenth century were considered, therefore, to be less important side phenomena. Nowadays, of course, the importance of electricity is well emphasized in the technical applications; however, the true significance of electricity in nature came to the fore only lately, in the development of atomic physics, when it turned out that almost all the phenomena we see around us in nature are based upon electric forces and their effects.

The first fact to notice is the existence of two kinds of electricity. An object can be charged with either one or the other kind. The two kinds are called positive and negative electricity, but no qualitative distinction is implied in these names. Positive electricity is not "better" than negative electricity. The people who named them could just as well have called the positive kind negative and vice versa. Charged objects exert a force upon each other. If they are charged with the same kind of electricity, they repel one another; if they are oppositely charged, they attract.

The electric charges of opposite kind can cancel each other. A positively charged object can be made electrically neutral if we transfer negative electricity of the same amount to it. Hence if an object is uncharged, it might contain either no electric charge at all, or an equal amount of positive charge and negative charge. It was one of the great discoveries of physics that uncharged matter actually does consist of a combination of positive and negative electricity.

Electric charges can move within matter. The motion of charge is particularly easy within metals. A metal wire connected to oppositely charged objects immediately discharges them, since opposite charges attract each other. The negative electricity of one object is drawn towards the positive charge of the other and vice versa. When a charge moves in a metal wire, we call it an electric current. Nowadays we have ready-made "charged objects" in our houses. The two ends in the electric outlets are kept constantly charged with opposite electricity, so that any wire between them gives us a current driven by the electric force between the outlet ends.

Careful investigation of what is moving in a wire has revealed that it is really the negative electricity that moves; the positive electricity stays with the object. The negative electricity consists of small atoms of electricity, the electrons, particles with which we shall have to deal at very much greater length in this book. All substances seem to be filled with electrons.

The negative charge of the electrons in matter normally is balanced by an equal amount of positive electricity. The positive charge, however, seems to be fixed to matter and thus immovable. Later we shall see that the positive charge is at the center of the atoms and therefore must remain with the atoms. Electrons can easily be removed from or added to any substance. If some electrons are added, the substance appears negatively charged; if some are removed, there is surplus of positive electricity and the substance appears positively charged.

Here we get the first insight into the electrical nature of matter. Superficially matter does not show its electricity; it is hidden by the fact that positive and negative charges in matter normally are balanced exactly, and we do not observe any over-all electric charge. Nevertheless, detailed evidence shows that matter actually is made up of electrically charged particles, the movable negative electrons and the centers of the atoms, which carry the positive charge.

Let us return to the force between charged objects. It depends on the distance between the charges. For example, the force between the opposite charges at the terminals of an ordinary electric outlet is too weak to drive electrons from one terminal to the other. If we bring the two ends close enough (about 1/100 inch), the force will be large enough to get electrons across, and we see a spark.

We can easily measure the force between two charged objects. The attractive force between a positively charged and a negatively charged particle decreases in proportion to the inverse square of the distance, somewhat as the gravitational attraction between two masses decreases with distance. Of course gravity acts between any two masses, whereas the electrical attraction acts only between two objects that are oppositely charged. When it acts between small charged objects, electrical attraction is usually very much greater than the gravitational force. This analogy brings us to a very fundamental point: the negative electrons in matter are attracted by the positive centers of the atoms in very much the same way the planets are attracted by the Sun. Hence we expect the electrons to circle around the atomic center as the planets circle around the Sun. This is a conclusion of great importance in the theory of the atom, as we shall see in the next chapter.

MAGNETISM

We are less often sensible of the phenomenon of magnetism in nature than we are of visible electric phenomena. To be sure, compasses work anywhere on Earth, any time, but we tend to take them for granted and ignore the physical implications. Although some of them are very common—iron, for instance—few metals show magnetic properties. Nevertheless magnetism is a striking phenomenon; when we hold a magnet and a piece of iron in our hands, we recognize that we are experiencing a special kind of force—a "force of nature" like gravity.

It was a great step forward when it became clear that magnetism is intimately connected with electricity. The connection between magnetic and electric phenomena was discovered by Hans Christian Oersted, a Dane, at the beginning of the nineteenth century. He found that an electric current in a circular or a spiral wire acts exactly like a magnet and creates a magnetic force. This discovery

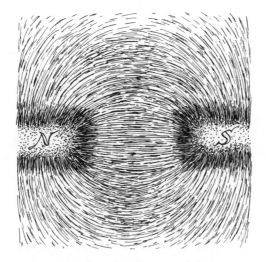

Figure 16. Magnetic field—iron filings

led André Ampère, a Frenchman, to the hypothesis that an ordinary steel magnet must work by the same principle, and he concluded that each atom must contain a small circular current which produces the magnetism if the majority of the atomic currents run in the same sense. His hypothesis has turned out to be entirely correct.

The connection between electricity and magnetism works in both directions. Not only does electricity create magnetism, but magnetism creates electricity. If any magnet is moved in the neighborhood of a metal wire or the wire is moved in the neighborhood of the magnet, a current is produced in the wire. The changing magnetic force has induced a current and, thus, has acted exactly like an electric force. This principle operates in our generators, the machines which produce the electric current we use. There coils of electric wire mounted on wheels are made to move through magnetic fields when the wheels rotate, and electric currents are produced in the wire. Whenever a magnetic field changes, it produces an electric force which sets electric charges into motion.

ELECTRIC AND MAGNETIC FIELDS

The study of the interactions of electric and magnetic effects led to the discovery of another phenomenon of nature, the electric and magnetic field. It came about in the middle of the nineteenth century, and the most important names associated with it are Michael Faraday, Maxwell, and Hertz. These new ideas not only have deeply influenced our ideas of nature, they also have revolutionized our way of life, since they brought with them the development of electrical power and radio transmission. The concept of the electric and magnetic field is connected with the strange fact that electric charges or magnets exert forces on other objects (charges or magnets) which are not in their immediate neighborhoods. The electric and magnetic force acts through space at a distance. How can this be? What transmits the effect from one body to the next?

In order to explain this action at a distance, we use the concept of a field. Every electric charge is the center or source of an electric field. This field is a property of empty space itself. The space in the neighborhood of the charge is in a state of tension. The tension can be measured by means of another charge, a test charge, which will experience a force wherever there is a field to exert one. Hence the attraction of a positive charge A and a negative charge B can be described as follows (See Figure 17): Charge A creates an electric

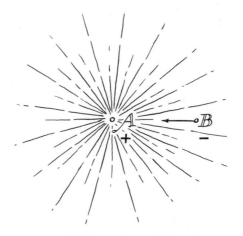

Figure 17. Electric field around a positive charge A. A state of tension is created in the space around A. The negative charge B is forced towards A.

field in the space around it. When charge B is placed in this field, it experiences the effect of this field in the form of a force which pushes it toward A. In the same way, of course, A is pushed toward B by the field of B.

Magnets create a similar field in the space surrounding them, the magnetic field. This is a different kind of "tension" in space. It acts on any piece of iron that is in this region of space; the "tension" takes the form of a force which pushes the iron toward the magnet.

So far the field concept seems to be only a complicated way to describe the forces between charges and the forces between magnets. However, the interaction of electric and magnetic phenomena shows that these fields actually have an existence of their own. Take the induction of a current in a wire by moving a magnet near the wire. When the magnet is moved, its magnetic field at the place of the wire changes in time: when the magnet comes nearer, the field increases; when it moves away, the field decreases. These changes induce a current in a wire; they bring charges into motion. Hence a changing magnetic field does what an electric field is supposed to do—a changing magnetic field creates an electric field.

Let us now consider the production of a magnetic field by electricity. Here a current produces a magnetic field. A current consists of moving charges, each of which carries an electric field. Thus we see that moving electric fields create magnetic fields, just as moving magnetic fields create electric ones.

ELECTROMAGNETIC WAVES

The relations between electric and magnetic fields occupied the physicists' minds through the first half of the nineteenth century. The man who contributed most to this problem, and who was able to bring mathematical order into this topic, was the great English theoretical physicist James Clerk Maxwell. The mathematical relations which connect the two fields and which are the basis of all our knowledge of electric phenomena are called the Maxwell equations. Their conception was a turning point in our understanding of nature, and it led to innumerable developments in physics and technology, of which the world of radio, radar, and television is only one of many.

Maxwell studied the relations between the two fields in detail and arrived at the following interesting question: If electric and magnetic fields are entities in themselves, shouldn't they exist independently of charges and magnets? Certainly static (unchanging) fields can exist only around charges and magnets, but what about changing fields? The fact that changing fields produce fields of the other kind suggests the possibility that this process might be self-per-petuating. A changing electric field creates a magnetic one; the latter field increases in the process of being created; hence it again creates a new electric field, and so forth. From the quantitative analysis of these relations, Maxwell could show simply that this proc-ess propagates in space—a varying electric field at one point produces a magnetic field in its neighborhood, which in turn pro-duces an electric field a little farther off, and so on. Therefore we obtain an electromagnetic oscillating field constantly expanding into space. Whenever a varying electric or magnetic field is produced —for example, by oscillating charges or magnets—the field will propagate in all directions. The speed of this propagation can be figured out from the observed strength of the currents induced by moving magnets and from the observed strength of the magnetic fields produced by currents. The result of this calculation was to fix the speed of propagation of electromagnetic fields at 3×10^8 meters/sec, and this is exactly the speed of *light*.

WHAT IS LIGHT?

It was one of the great moments in the history of science when Maxwell completed those calculations. He used only the measure-ments of electric currents and magnetic fields, phenomena which have seemingly nothing to do with light, and he concluded from these measurements that oscillating electric fields propagate like waves through space, exactly with the velocity of light signals. A connection was discovered between two parts of physics which appeared to be totally unconnected: optics and electricity.

From Maxwell's calculations it was then only a small step, but still a bold one, to conclude that light is nothing but a propagation of electromagnetic fields. With this recognition many scattered facts fall into order. For example, we understand immediately why all matter emits light when heated to a high temperature. It comes from the electric composition of matter. At high temperature the charged particles of matter, in particular the electrons, perform intense and rapid motions; therefore they create rapidly changing electric fields which initiate the propagation of fields into space with light velocity; light is emitted.

If Maxwell's idea of the electromagnetic nature of light is correct, one should be able to produce new kinds of light. Any electric charge or magnet, set into oscillation, would generate electromagnetic fields propagating into space, and would act as a source of light at a frequency equal to the frequency of the oscillations.

For example, an oscillating current in a wire would send out electromagnetic waves, and one might pick them up at a large distance if he exposed another wire to the waves and observed the weak currents induced in it. This experiment was first done in 1880 by Hertz, who wanted to prove the correctness of Maxwell's ideas. Hertz's success opened up a whole new technology. Today space is full of such waves. They are the radio waves which are produced by alternating currents in antennas, and they differ from ordinary light waves only in their frequency and wave length. Evidently the current oscillations that we set up artificially in our antennas are much slower than the oscillations of electrons heated in a light bulb. So the radio waves are light, but with much lower frequency and consequently much longer wave length. (See Figure 18.)

Now we also can answer the question about the nature of light waves: what is it that oscillates and what carries the wave? It is the electric-and-magnetic-field strength that performs the oscillations. The carrier of the wave is space itself, since the electromagnetic fields are properties of space; they are space under tension. The electric and magnetic tensions travel through space as light, just as the compression and dilution of air travels through air as sound. An electromagnetic wave is a double wave: electric- and magnetic-field strengths travel together and are intimately interwoven. Thus light is electromagnetic. It is electromagnetism in its purest form: Light is a wave of electromagnetic fields traveling through space, separated from the electric charges which have produced them.

Maxwell's discovery is comparable in its importance to Newton's discovery of the law of gravity. Newton connected the phenomenon of planetary motion with the phenomenon of gravity on Earth and discovered the fundamental laws governing the mechanical motion of masses under the influence of forces. Maxwell connected optics with electricity and discovered the fundamental laws (the Maxwell equations) that govern the behavior of electric and magnetic fields and their interaction with charges and magnets. With Newton's work the concept of a universal law of gravity was introduced; Maxwell's work established the concept of the electromagnetic field and its propagation in space.

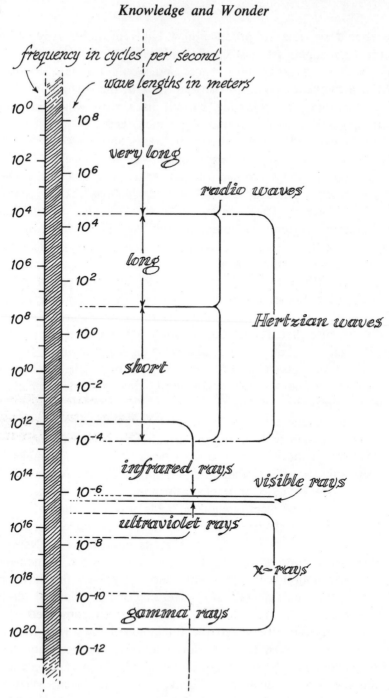

Figure 18. Electromagnetic spectrum.

ATOMS

Chapter Four

THE NATURAL UNITS OF MATTER

In our world we find an overwhelming variety of different substances with most complicated structures and properties, in particular when we look at living matter. In order to get at the fundamental features of the structure of matter, we must begin our study with simple substances. At the start we shall not consider organic substances, such as wood or the skin of our bodies, whose structure is intricate and seems to be a complicated combination of substructures. We first consider homogeneous substances such as air, water, oil, or a piece of metal or a sample of rock. These substances occur in three states of aggregation—in the solid state, in the liquid state, and in the gaseous state as vapors. In the solid and liquid states matter seems to be densely packed; it is extremely difficult to compress matter in these states. In the gaseous state compression is very easy; therefore one would conclude that matter in a gas is dilute, that there is empty space between the units of matter.

What are those units of matter? Do units indeed exist? Can we subdivide a certain amount of a given substance indefinitely or is there a smallest amount? The answer to this fundamental question is well known today. There is a smallest unit of every substance and it is called a molecule, and in some substances an atom. The difference between an atom and a molecule will be taken up in the last section of this chapter. Until then we do not need to distinguish between those two types of smallest units. The units are very small, and most of the simple substances give the impression of homogeneity. However, investigations with very fine instruments reveal that there is a molecular structure. Plate III, for example, shows a picture of the tip of a very fine tungsten needle, taken with a so-called field-ion microscope, a device with which one can locate extremely small details on some metallic surfaces. Here we see a regular structure of the units of which tungsten seems to consist. We can calculate from the magnification of this microscope how small the units are, and we find that they measure roughly 3×10^{-8} centimeters. Then one gram of tungsten would contain about 3×10^{21} of these units.[1] We also infer from this picture that in the solid state the units form a regular lattice in a well-established order.

The molecular nature of a gas, such as air, can be shown in a very impressive way. We know that air can move light objects; it is moving air that sets the leaves of a tree rustling. But if air is kept at rest in a container with no wind or current, we do not expect to detect any movement of objects that are suspended in the still air. If the objects are very small and light, perhaps very small particles of dust or smoke, our expectation is in for a shock. If you look through a microscope at particles suspended in air, you will notice that they undergo small irregular displacements here or there. (See Figure 19.) It looks as if they were being hit with invisible tiny bullets fired at them at random from all directions. This irregular motion of small particles was first discovered by a botanist, Robert Brown, in 1827, when through his microscope he found small particles performing this random dance. The particles he observed were immersed in water and not in air, but the principle involved is the same.

This "Brownian motion" is direct evidence that air is not con-

---

[1] The size of the tungsten units—they are atoms of tungsten—is an inch divided by 100 million. We can use our experience from the first chapter to appreciate this small size. The breadth of hair is 10,000 smaller than the length of an outstretched arm (one meter). 100 million is 10,000 times 10,000. Hence the size of the tungsten atom is to the size of one inch as the breadth of a hair is to ten kilometers (six miles).

The atoms in tungsten are so arranged that they touch each other. Hence a cube of tungsten whose height is n times the site of the atom contains n^3 atoms. A gram of tungsten in cube form would have a height of 0.4 centimeter. This is fourteen million times the size of an atom. Hence there are (14 million)^3 atoms in a gram of tungsten. This is about 3×10^{21} atoms.

Plate III. This remarkable photograph of the arrangement of tungsten atoms was made with a field-ion microscope.

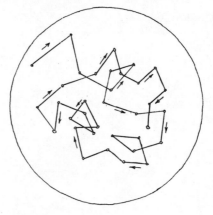

Figure 19. Brownian motion. A light particle suffers irregular displacements in air if seen through a microscope.

tinuous, but consists of many small units flying through space in all directions at random and in an irregular pattern. Any object in air is bombarded at random from all sides by the molecules, and this bombardment produces the air pressure. Ordinarily the number of hits is so large that it causes a continuous pressure effect. If the object is very small, however, there are far fewer hits and, as a consequence, individual hits can have an extra effect from time to time. This is the cause of the Brownian motion.

We can learn about the smallest units of liquids by asking a question: How large an area can we cover with a thin film of liquid when we have only a given quantity of liquid at our disposition? If there were no smallest unit, one could cover any area with a film of one gram liquid, since one could always double the area by making the film half as thick. But if a smallest unit does exist, the thickness of the film cannot be less than the size of this unit, and there must be a largest area over which a given quantity of liquid can spread.

This experiment can be performed very easily by spreading a quantity of oil on a water surface. It turns out that a little droplet of oil, one millimeter across, spreads over as much as thirty square feet, but never farther. We conclude, therefore, that there is a smallest unit of oil. We can calculate from the size of the area how large the unit is, and we get roughly 3×10^{-8} centimeters for the size of the oil unit, not very different from the tungsten atom.[2]

---

[2] Let us assume that the drop of oil one millimeter across has the shape of a cube one millimeter high. Let us then reassemble the cube by cutting the thirty square

The existence of a definite smallest unit in every substance supplies us with an absolute measure of quantity. Ordinarily we speak of one pound of iron, one gallon of water, a cubic foot of air under atmospheric pressure. All these measures depend on arbitrary conventions of measurement. But when we refer to one million iron atoms, one million water or air molecules, then we have made use of an absolute measure that is characteristic of the substance and is independent of any human convention. Matter can be "counted" instead of weighed or measured.

Since the molecules or atoms are such extremely tiny quantities from our human point of view, the chemists prefer to use as an absolute measure of matter a "mole" of a substance. This is a fixed number of smallest units; for practical reasons, the number of atoms in one gram of hydrogen has been chosen to define the mole. It is the

AVOGADRO'S NUMBER 6.03×10^{23}

Figure 20.

famous number of Avogadro, 6.03×10^{23}. (See Figure 20.) One mole of water, which is 6.03×10^{23} water molecules, fills a little more than a cubic inch; one mole of rock (quartz) fills about 4/3 cubic inches, and one mole of air under normal conditions is contained in ¾ of a cubic foot. The mole of water and the mole of quartz fill roughly the same space, so the size of their smallest units must be about equal. The mole of air, however, fills a much larger volume than the mole of water and rock. This is not because of the large size of the unit; it is because air is a gas, with its molecules far apart from each other, flying freely around in space. When we cool air to such a low temperature that it becomes a liquid (the molecules then touch each other), the volume of a mole is roughly the same as for water.

---

feet of oil sheet into small squares of one millimeter size and piling them up on top of each other. The pile will reach a height of one millimeter—the height of the original cube. Thirty square feet contain three million square millimeters. Hence the thickness of the oil sheet is one millimeter divided by three million. This gives about 3×10^{-8} centimeters, which is then the size of the oil unit, the molecule of oil.

HEAT

What makes an object hot or cold? For a long time people believed that heat was a substance contained in a hot object. When in contact with a cold object, the heat substance, they said, diffused into the cold object and thus equalized the temperature. In the middle of the last century it became clear, however, that heat is energy, specifically the energy of random motion of the molecules or atoms. When a sample of matter is heated, all that changes is that the smallest units perform faster and more energetic random motions.

Let us look at a few examples. In the tungsten needle we saw the tungsten atoms arranged in a regular pattern. How can they perform random motions? When heated, they vibrate and oscillate around their assigned places in the regular structure. Indeed this back-and-forth motion is partially responsible for the fuzziness of the picture in Plate III. At higher temperature the picture would become even fuzzier. If we raise the temperature very much, the vibrations reach as far as the distances to the next neighbors, and the regular arrangement is destroyed. This happens when the heat is high enough to melt the metal.

In a gas such as air the heat motion of the molecules is the ordinary straight motion of each molecule when the molecules fly at random through space, colliding with each other and with the walls. The higher the temperature, the faster the motion. On a cold day (0° Fahrenheit) the average speed of an air molecule is around 400 meters per second (900 miles per hour); on a hot day (100° Fahrenheit) it is about 440 meters per second (1000 miles per hour). The difference between a very hot and a very cold day is only 10 per cent difference in speed of the air molecules. We notice this difference of molecular speed in the pressure of automobile tires. The air pressure is caused by the impact of the molecules' colliding with the walls, and this impact is proportional to the square of the speed. A 10 per cent drop in speed causes a 20 per cent drop of impacts; hence when the temperature falls from 100° to 0° Fahrenheit, the tire pressure drops by 20 per cent.

In spite of the tremendous speed of air molecules at ordinary temperatures, the molecules don't travel very far. Collisions with other molecules constantly interrupt their flight. In air their average free and uninterrupted flying path is only one hundred thousandth of a centimeter. Hence their flight is more like a fast random motion at the previously mentioned speed, but with a change of direction after every hundred-thousandth centimeter.

Heat motion in any material, solid or gas, ceases completely at a temperature of −459° Fahrenheit, which is also called zero-degree absolute temperature. This is the temperature at which all molecular random motion is frozen still, and it is obviously the lowest possible temperature.

MOLECULES AND ATOMS

Can the smallest units of matter be broken up into even smaller parts? They can, but the parts are no longer the same substance. A molecule of water is the smallest unit of water. A part of the molecule is no longer water, it is hydrogen or oxygen.

It is much harder to break a molecule into smaller parts than to break a substance into its molecules. For example, when we boil water and produce steam, we have broken up the substance water into its molecules. In the form of steam, water is a gas whose smallest units fly about in space, each molecule separated from the other, but each molecule itself remains an unbroken unit. When we discharge a strong electric spark through steam, however, some of the molecules will be broken, and we get hydrogen and oxygen gas. The spark is a much stronger energy source than the process of boiling. In some cases intense heating breaks up the molecules and thus changes one substance into another.

In the development of chemistry through the ages we have come to recognize that certain substances can be decomposed into others by intense heat, electric sparks, or other violent treatments, and that two substances can be compounded to form a new substance, a chemical compound. Hydrogen and oxygen can be compounded into water, and a piece of quartz can be decomposed into silicon and oxygen.

One of the most exciting moments in the history of mankind must have been the time about 3000 B.C. when a man first put certain earthlike substances, perhaps cuprite or galena, on a charcoal fire. Out came a new substance, metallic copper or lead. Most metals such as iron, copper, lead, zinc, etc., are truly man-made substances; they rarely occur in nature except for the very small amounts of native ores (copper, for instance) and nickel-iron

A, B—Two furnaces. C—Forehearth. D—Dipping-pots. The master stands at the one furnace and draws away the slags with an iron fork. E—Iron fork. F—Wooden hoe with which the cakes of melted pyrites are drawn out. G—The forehearth crucible: one-half inside is to be seen open in the other furnace. H—The half outside the furnace. I—The assistant prepares the forehearth, which is separated from the furnace that it may be seen. K—Bar. L—Wooden rammer. M—Ladder. N—Ladle.

Figure 21. Woodcut illustration from 16th century book on metallurgy depicting blast furnaces for the smelting of copper and lead ores. A, B—Two furnaces. C—Forehearth. D—Dipping-pots. The master stands at the one furnace and draws away the slags with an iron fork. E—Iron fork. F—Wooden hoe with which the cakes of melted pyrites are drawn out. G—The forehearth crucible: one-half inside is to be seen open in the other furnace. H—The half outside the furnace. I—The assistant prepares the forehearth, which is separated from the furnace that it may be seen. K—Bar. L—Wooden rammer. M—Ladder. N—Ladle.

alloys that come from outer space in meteorites. There is a simple reason: pure metals do not last when exposed to the oxygen in air. Most metals combine with oxygen in time and form chemical compounds, which are the same earthlike substances from which they had been extracted. Man can transform these ores into pure metals for long enough periods for practical use, but only very short ones compared to the age of the earth.

The study of the processes in which substances are changed into other substances has revealed a significant fact: All, really all, existing substances can be decomposed into ninety-two fundamental substances, which are called the elements. Any piece of matter, wherever found and in whatever state of aggregation, is always either an element or consists of several elements. A substance whose smallest unit is a combination of several elements is called a chemical compound.

Many familiar substances are actually elements. All pure metals, such as gold, silver, iron, lead, aluminum, etc., are elements. Many gases, such as hydrogen, oxygen, or nitrogen, are also elements, but other gases, such as illuminating gas or carbon dioxide, are compounds. Most well-known liquids are chemical compounds. The smallest unit of an element is called an atom. The smallest unit of a chemical compound is called a molecule. Since all chemical compounds can be decomposed into elements, the smallest unit of a chemical compound must be made up of the smallest units of elements. Hence each molecule is a conglomeration of atoms; it consists of the atoms of those elements that make up the chemical compound. They fit together and form a stable unit, the molecule, which is endowed with all the properties of the substance of which it is the unit.

Water is a chemical compound of hydrogen and oxygen. The smallest units of the elements hydrogen and oxygen are the hydrogen atoms and the oxygen atoms.[3] The smallest unit of water is the water molecule, which consists of two hydrogen atoms and one oxygen

[3] There is one fact that often gives rise to confusion: For many elements the smallest unit is not a single atom of the element but a conglomeration of two of these atoms, tightly bound to form a pair of equal atoms. This is true of most of the elements appearing as gases—hydrogen, oxygen, etc. Hence their smallest units are also molecules, but molecules consisting of a pair of equal atoms (H_2, O_2, etc.). If such a molecule is broken, the process does not change the substance. For the sake of clarity, however, we always consider the atom as the smallest unit of an element.

atom (H_2O), so tightly bound together that only an electric spark can break them apart.

There are small and large molecules. The molecule of water consists of only three atoms; a molecule of ethyl alcohol consists of nine atoms: one oxygen, two carbon, and six hydrogen atoms. Some molecules occurring in living matter, such as proteins, contain hundreds of thousands of atoms.

The discovery of the ninety-two elements and their atoms was the most important step toward the understanding of the structure of matter. It took a long time for the ideas to clear and the facts to be recognized. The concept of basic substances of which all other substances can be made is as old as natural philosophy. Many Greek philosophers speculated with ideas of this kind. The first conclusions similar to our present ones were drawn by Robert Boyle in the seventeenth century, although many of the substances which he thought were elements turned out to be chemical compounds. The famous French chemist Antoine Lavoisier, who was killed in the French Revolution, made a list of thirty-three elements. The present list of elements and the interpretation of molecules as being combinations of atoms of elements were developed in the nineteenth century, and the most important work came from the English chemist John Dalton.

Let us be aware of the immense impact of this discovery. We are surrounded by an infinite variety of substances with different and ever changing forms, shapes, and qualities, hot or cold, living or dead. In spite of this immense variety, everything we know about is made of only ninety-two different kinds of atoms, each kind belonging to a well-defined, specific element. Nothing is ever found in living or non-living matter that cannot be decomposed into some of the ninety-two elements. This discovery revealed a basic simplicity in the structure of matter. We have to deal with combinations of a relatively small number of fundamental units. Hence there is some hope that the principles underlying the structure of matter are simple enough to be grasped by the human mind.

THE INTERNAL STRUCTURE OF ATOMS

It is of basic importance to learn more about the structure of the atoms themselves. We must find out what it is that exists in ninety-two different forms and is endowed with an ability to combine and produce the great variety of known substances; we must be able to understand why certain combinations are possible and others are not; and finally, we must try to get some understanding how such highly organized systems as living matter can originate.

The ninety-two kinds of atoms have very different properties. Some form gases; some form metals; some, such as the carbon atoms, are able to combine easily with other atoms and form the backbone of many chemical compounds; while others, the atoms of helium, neon, or argon, for example, combine almost never. In spite of these differences, the atoms all seem to be roughly of equal size. We can see this in the following way:

When we know the atomic constitution of the molecule of a substance, we can find out easily how many atoms are contained in a given amount of that substance. Let us remember that a mole of water is that quantity containing 6.03×10^{23} molecules, and that this quantity fills a little more than a cubic inch. Since a molecule contains three atoms (two hydrogen and one oxygen atom), the mole of water contains about 18×10^{23} atoms. So one cubic inch of water then contains a little less than this number of atoms. We get a similar but smaller value for the number of atoms in a cubic inch of rock: one mole of quartz fills $4/3$ cubic inches. One molecule of quartz consists also of three atoms, one silicon and two oxygen. Hence the number of atoms in a cubic inch is $\frac{3}{4} \times 18 \times 10^{23} = 13.5 \times 10^{23}$ atoms. Even when taking very different substances, liquids or solids such as gold or wood or carbon, one always gets something between 10 and 25 times 10^{23} for the number of atoms per cubic inch. Since in liquids and solids the molecules are closely packed, and the atoms are also closely packed within the molecules, we conclude that all atoms are roughly of the same size: about 10 to 25×10^{23} per cubic inch. This means that the size of an atom is a few 10^{-8} centimeters across.

What do we know about the internal structure of atoms? Here we come to a fundamental question—the mechanisms which we find in the atoms must be the clue to an explanation of the properties of the matter we see around us. It became clear in the last chapter that electricity plays an important role, and that the electrons are an essential part of the atom. The decisive experiments, however, were made in 1910 by Ernest Rutherford, Hans Geiger, and E. Marsden, who probed the structure of the atom with alpha particles, the very fast electrically charged particles emitted by some radioactive substances. They directed a beam of these particles into a slab of metal and observed where and how much the direction of motion of the particles changed when penetrating the metal (See Figure 22).

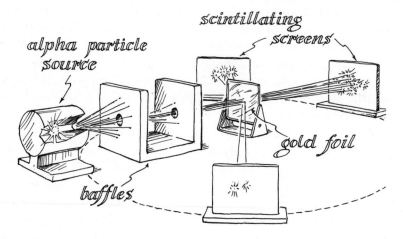

Figure 22. Rutherford Experiment.

These measurements tell us something about how the electricity is distributed in the atoms of the metal. If electric charge is spread smoothly over the atom, the alpha particle on its flight through the atom would experience smooth electric forces and would never be strongly deviated from its path. If electricity is concentrated at certain points in the atom, however, the alpha particle would be strongly influenced whenever it came near these points. It is worth while to quote Rutherford's own description of this experiment:

". . . I would like to use this example to show how you often stumble upon facts by accident. In the early days I had observed the scattering of α-particles, and Dr. Geiger in my laboratory had examined it in detail. He found, in thin pieces of heavy metal that the scattering was usually small, of the order of one degree. One day Geiger came to me and said, 'Don't you think that young Marsden, whom I am training in radioactive methods, ought to begin a small research?' Now I had thought that too, so I said, 'Why not let him see if any α-particles can be scattered through a large angle?' I may tell you in confidence that I did not believe that they would be, since we knew that the α-particle was a very fast, massive particle, with a great deal of energy, and you could show that if the scattering was due to the accumulated effect of a number of small scatterings the chance of an α-particle's being scattered backwards was very small. Then I remember two or three days later Geiger coming to me in great excitement and saying, 'We have been able to get some of the α-particles coming backwards . . .' It was quite the most incredible event that has ever happened to me in my life. It was almost as incredible as if you fired a 15-inch shell at a piece of tissue paper and it came back and hit you. On consideration, I realized that this scattering backwards must be the result of a single collision, and when I made calculations I saw that it was impossible to get anything of that order of magnitude unless you took a system in which the greater part of the mass of the atom was concentrated in a minute nucleus. It was then that I had the idea of an atom with a minute massive center carrying a charge. I worked out mathematically what laws the scattering should obey, and I found that the number of particles scattered through a given angle should be proportional to the thickness of the scattering foil, the square of the nuclear charge, and inversely proportional to the fourth power of the velocity. These deductions were later verified by Geiger and Marsden in a series of beautiful experiments."[4]

With these experiments and many others that followed, it was shown beyond doubt that the atom consists of a positively charged, small but massive nucleus, in which most of the weight of the atom resides, surrounded by negatively charged electrons, which are much lighter than the nucleus. The actual size of the nucleus is extremely small. Its diameter is between 10^{-13} and 10^{-12} centimeters, depending upon the kind of the atom; it is therefore about 10,000 times smaller than the atom itself, but quite heavy since it contains almost all the mass. Rutherford and other physicists, in particular Moseley, determined the number of electrons in each atom and the charge of the atomic nucleus. Since the total atom is uncharged, the negatively charged electrons must balance the charge of the positively charged nucleus. Hence the number of electrons must always be equal to the charge of the nucleus expressed in units of electronic charges. This number is characteristic of each kind of atom. Hydrogen, for example, has one electron and one positive-charge unit in the nucleus; helium has two electrons, lithium three, etc., up to uranium with ninety-two electrons and a nucleus charged with ninety-two positive-charge units. This number is called the

[4] E. Rutherford, "The Development of the Theory of Atomic Structure," from *Background to Modern Science* (Macmillan, New York, 1940).

atomic number Z. Every element has its characteristic atomic number Z, which gives the positive charge of the nucleus and also the number of electrons in the atom.

With this discovery the qualitative difference between the ninety-two elements was reduced to a quantitative one: Atoms of one element differ from those of the others only by the number of electrons, a number which also determines how many positive-charge units there are in the nucleus.

One can order the atoms according to the atomic number Z, and each number from 1 to 92, except technetium (43) and promethium (61), corresponds to an element found in nature. Here is the number Z for the most important elements:

Hydrogen	1	Nitrogen	7	Silicon	14	Gold	79
Helium	2	Oxygen	8	Iron	26	Lead	92
Lithium	3	Sodium	11	Silver	47	Uranium	92
Carbon	6						

There can also exist artificially produced elements, the so-called "transuranic" elements, which have more than ninety-two electrons. They have short lifetimes and do not occur in nature under normal conditions.

THE GREAT PROBLEMS OF ATOMIC STRUCTURE

This reduction of the qualitative differences among ninety-two kinds of atoms to a quantitative one represented an enormous step forward. But every great scientific discovery creates new problems when it solves old ones. When we know more, we have more questions to ask. Our knowledge is an island in the infinite ocean of the unknown, and the larger this island grows, the more extended are its boundaries toward the unknown. The recognition of structure in the atom immediately poses a question. How can those quantitative differences of structure be the cause of the observed qualitative differences in the properties of the elements? How is it possible, for example, that bromine, with thirty-five electrons, is a brownish liquid forming many characteristic chemical compounds, while krypton, with thirty-six electrons, is a gas forming no compound at all, and rubidium, with thirty-seven electrons, is a metal? Why should one electron more or one electron less make such a great difference in the properties of the atom? This question was not answered until later, when the quantum nature of matter was understood. It will be the subject of the next chapter.

What motions do we expect in the atom? When Rutherford found out that the atom consists of a massive positive center surrounded by light negative electrons, it was obvious that the atom must be very similar to a planetary system. The electrons are attracted to the center by the electric attraction between opposite charges. This force is much stronger than the force of gravity between the nucleus and the electron, but it obeys the same law in its dependence on the distance—it decreases with the square of the distance. We therefore expect the electrons to move around the nucleus in much the same way the planets move around the sun. Electric attraction between nucleus and electron replaces the force of gravity. An atom should be a small planetary system, and each kind of atom would have a different number of planet electrons. We might expect to find in the small world of the atom a replica of the big world in the sky.

In some respects this expectation seemed to be satisfied. For example, we can calculate what number of revolutions an electron would make around the nucleus per second, say, in hydrogen. We know the size of the orbit—it is about as big as the hydrogen atom, roughly 10^{-8} centimeters. We then know the force with which the electron is attracted, and we can figure out the speed at which it must circle the nucleus in order to make the centrifugal force equal to the attractive force. This calculation gives about 10^{16} revolutions per second, which means that the "year" of the atomic solar system—the time the planet takes to get around once—is as short as 10^{-16} seconds. This number can be put to a test. We know that oscillating electric charges radiate light and that the frequency of this light (the number of ups and downs of the light wave per second) must be equal to the number of the oscillations per second of the electric charge. Therefore we should expect that the light emitted by a hydrogen atom has a frequency of 10^{16} per second. In fact, incandescent hydrogen gas does radiate light of that frequency.

But the planetary atomic model soon runs into great difficulties. If the atom were a true planetary system in which electric charges are constantly circling the nucleus, the revolving electrons should emit light all the time, in ordinary cool hydrogen as well as in hydrogen incandescent under very high temperatures. This does not happen. There is another important shortcoming: the light of hydrogen gas, and of any other gas too, is emitted and also absorbed only at definite frequencies, which are characteristic of the element making up the gas. It is as if every atomic species is a radio station to which have been assigned certain specific frequencies for transmitting and receiving activities. The spectroscopists have studied these assignments over many decades. The frequencies provide an excellent tool for the identification of elements; it is as if one would identify a radio station by looking up its frequency in the lists of radio transmitters. It is the only way to get information about the chemical compositions of the stars.

Now it is very difficult to reconcile this situation with a planetary system structure. There are many possible orbits around the center. In some of these orbits around the nucleus, the electron circles faster and in others slower. The question arises why the electron should circle only in those orbits which have the assigned frequency. It is all the more incomprehensible since we know that in a gas the atoms collide with each other about 10^{12} times a second (that, on the average, is once in 10,000 hydrogen-atom years). The energy of these collisions can be deduced from the heat energy in a gas. The impacts are quite powerful and should change the orbits of the electrons completely in respect to their size, shape, and frequency. How then is it possible that they keep their assigned frequencies?

In order to illustrate this question more vividly, let us consider a sample of sodium gas. It absorbs only light that has the particular frequency assigned to the sodium atom. When heated up, sodium emits the well-known yellow sodium light, its assigned frequency. Let us now condense the gas to a solid piece of sodium metal by cooling or compressing. In the metal the atoms touch each other and therefore the planetary orbits intermesh. We shall not be astonished to find that the metal does not respond particularly to the frequency assigned to the free sodium atom. In fact, the metal does not seem to have any particular frequency of response, as one might expect of a complicated intermesh of electron orbits. Let us then transform the metal back into sodium gas by evaporation. The gas will have exactly the same properties as before: it will absorb and emit only the frequencies typical for the sodium atom.

This behavior is utterly at variance with, and completely incomprehensible on, the basis of a planetary atomic model. These are properties one would never expect of a planetary system. How could we imagine that the electrons will find their way into exactly the same orbits when the atoms are evaporated from the metal? There is not the slightest reason for it. In fact it would appear improbable to the highest degree that the orbits after evaporation will be similar at all to the orbits before evaporation, except in general shape and in approximate size. But what we do find is an equality of frequency and of many other features, to a degree that is accurate to the most minute details. It is as if the planet Venus, after having been knocked out of its orbit in some collision with another star, should obediently glide back into its previous orbit when the star has gone.

We are accustomed to find in nature substances with well-defined and reproducible properties. It is deeply ingrained in our way of thinking that nature is so, and we are not at all astonished that, for example, two atoms of gold, mined at different locations and processed in different ways, end up identical, indistinguishable from one another. All our lives are built upon the experience that substances have their characteristic properties; we are able to recognize metals, minerals, and chemicals and to distinguish between different kinds of substances on the basis of their characteristic and ever recurring properties. Gold always has the properties of gold, and the seed of a zinnia will produce zinnias every spring.

We must realize, however, that all this remains incomprehensible on the basis of the planetary model of the atom. Not only is it beyond explanation, but it is opposed to the most characteristic features of a planetary system. The structure of the orbits is bound to depend upon the initial conditions; there are many possible forms and shapes of the orbits, which depend on the previous history of the system. Only very rarely would two atoms of the same kind exhibit identical properties if they were ordinary planetary systems.

Let us summarize the situation: All about us nature exhibits characteristic and specific properties of various materials. In spite of the overwhelming variety of substances, each substance is reproducible and recurrent with all its characteristic properties. For this situation to exist, the atoms must have three properties:

1. *Stability.* The atoms keep their specific properties in spite of heavy collisions and other perturbations to which they are subjected.
2. *Identity.* All atoms of the same kind (same electron number Z)

exhibit identical properties; they emit and absorb the same frequencies, they have exactly the same size, shape, and internal motion.

3. *Regeneration.* If an atom is distorted and its electron orbits forced to change by high pressure or by close neighboring atoms, it regains its exact original shape and orbits when the cause of distortion is removed.

Experiments indicate, however, that the atom is a planetary system of electrons circling around the nucleus, a system which should never exhibit these three properties. Hence this picture of the atoms cannot explain at all the specificity of material qualities. We must find a new and essential trait in the structure of the atom that is not contained in the classical picture of the atom as a planetary system. This new insight into the nature of the atom was provided by the development of quantum theory.

THE QUANTUM

Chapter Five

The world of atoms is full of the unexpected. When we try to penetrate into the inner structure of the atom, we observe strange things which appear contradictory because they are so different from our experience with ordinary large-scale matter. Seemingly they do not make sense to our accustomed ideas of what particles are and how they should behave. We are aware that something new and unusual must be found if we are to explain the facts of nature as we see them around us.

In the last chapter we stressed the serious contradictions afflicting the study of the structure of the atom. On the one hand the atom revealed itself as a small planetary system of circulating electrons; on the other hand we find a stability and an exhibition of characteristic properties completely foreign to a planetary system. In this chapter we start out with a more detailed account of further unusual observations concerning atoms and atomic particles, and hope to find our way to the new phenomena that govern the interior of atoms. It will not be a historical account. In the actual progress of science, unfortunately, a discovery is rarely made at the time when it could be most useful for our understanding; it does not come until technological development has created the means of performing the necessary measurements. Here we will put the new discoveries into an order that makes it easier to discern the deeper sense in them. We discuss three groups of observations, each one revealing strange and uncommon features of the atomic world.

The first group contains the discoveries of quantum states in the atom, the second deals with the quantum nature of light, and the third with the wave properties of material particles. Then we should be ready to understand the essential content of the new quantum mechanics, which is based upon these discoveries. It is the framework of our present understanding of atomic phenomena.

THE QUANTUM STATES OF THE ATOM

In 1913 James Franck and Gustav Hertz performed a series of experiments in which they attempted to change the planetary orbits of the electrons in the atom. They argued this way: The atom seems to resist changes of its electron orbits. Let us try to change these orbits by force and see how, and how much, the atom can resist. We would expect that the orbits of the planets would be changed if a star should pass close to our solar system. Franck and Hertz arranged an experiment in the atomic world that would correspond to such a solar cataclysm. In simple terms, their experiment was this: We have a container filled with a gas of atoms, perhaps sodium or hydrogen atoms (Figure 23). We pass a straight beam of electrons through the gas. Since electrons have a strong electric effect on each other, we expect that an electron of the beam, when passing near an atom, will influence the orbiting electrons in the atom and change their orbits, just as a nearby passing star would change the orbit of the Earth.

We cannot look directly at the electron orbits and see whether they have been changed, but we can find out indirectly what has happened. We make sure that in the beam of electrons all electrons have exactly the same speed when they enter the gas. Any change the electrons may cause in the atom will be associated with a change of speed of the electrons. This prediction follows from the law of conservation of energy. Energy is needed to alter the orbit of an electron in an atom;[1] hence, if the orbit is changed by a beam elec-

---

[1] Whenever something happens in nature, energy is exchanged: If I rap on the table with my finger, energy is transmitted from my body to the table, and the energy of my body is reduced by this amount. I shall have to eat again in order to replenish it.

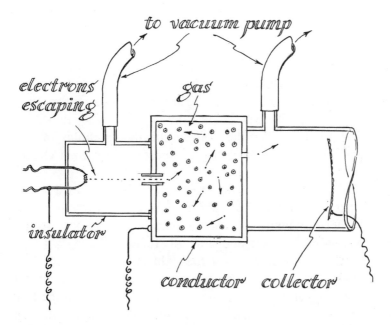

Figure 23. The general idea of an experiment to measure the changes in the energy of electrons when they collide with gas atoms. The electrons pass through a sample of gas (sodium vapor) in the middle chamber. Electrons leave the gun with energy given by the accelerating voltage applied at the two wires on the left side. Their energy remaining after collisions is measured in the right-hand chamber.

tron passing by, this electron must lose some energy. Speed is energy; therefore the electron's speed will be reduced, and this reduction can be observed when the beam leaves the gas on the other side. The same would happen if a star passed by our solar system. Its passing would give a push to the Earth, thus increasing the Earth's energy and decreasing the energy of the star.

What should we expect on the basis of the planetary model? There should be all kinds of changes of orbits, small and large, depending upon how close the electron has passed by an atom. We should expect energy losses (or sometimes gains) ranging over all values from zero up; the average loss should be less when the beam goes through a more dilute gas, since there then would be fewer close approaches.

The observations turned out to be completely different. No change of speed at all was observed if the initial energy of the electrons was less than a certain minimum. This minimum energy was quite high —more than a hundred times greater than the heat energy of electrons at ordinary temperatures. When the energy was higher than that minimum, the electrons lost either certain specific amounts of energy or none at all. These specific amounts, and also the minimum, are characteristic of the kind of atom in the gas; they do not depend on the density of the gas or on any other external circumstances. What can this strange result mean? It tells us that one cannot change the electron orbits in the atom by any arbitrary amount. Either they do not change at all, or they change by specific, and rather large, amounts of energy. Here the concept of the quantum of energy comes in. Energy can be fed into an atom only in certain characteristic quanta—no more, or less.

It is as if the atom accepts energy only in predetermined lumps. It does not take a small bite, but only the full lump. Every atom has its own characteristic lumps of energy that it can accept. If less is offered, the atom does not budge at all. In fact it budges (changes its state) only if it is offered just the right amount.

This situation is certainly foreign to our picture of a planetary system. A passing star can feed any amount of energy into the Earth's orbit. The greater the distance of passing, the smaller the energy transferred. But the result of our experiment is not so startling in view of what we already know about the atom. It shows that the state of the atom has an intrinsic stability. Weak impacts cannot change it, only a large amount of energy. There must be something that keeps the atom in its normal characteristic state, and that something can be overcome only with large energies. May it not be the same phenomenon that gives rise to the specificity of the atoms, that always forces the electrons back into the configuration characteristic of the special type of atom?

We must be more quantitative now. What is the minimum energy necessary to change the state of an atom? Let us digress here in order to learn how one expresses energies in atomic problems. We measure energy of atomic particles by a unit called "electron volt." It is the energy an electron would receive from a voltage of one volt. The voltage is the "pressure" of electricity at an electric outlet. For example, the outlets in our houses have a voltage pressure of 120 volts, which forces the current through our electric bulbs or appliances. If electrons could move freely between the terminals of an electric outlet of 120 volts, as we have them in our houses, they would be expelled with an energy of 120 electron volts. Actually no free electron can exist in the air; if there were any, they would be caught quickly by the air molecules. Hence an ordinary open outlet does not expel electrons. But if one leads the terminals of the outlet into a region of very low air pressure (few molecules), one sees a glow around the wires, caused by the electrons expelled with an energy up to 120 electron volts of energy.

The electron volt is a convenient unit of energy for our problems. For example, in air of ordinary temperature the molecules fly to and fro with an average kinetic energy of 1/30 electron volt. This is the average energy per atom of any kind of heat motion at room temperature; it is, for example, the energy of the irregular heat oscillations that atoms perform in a piece of metal, the ones that cause melting at higher temperatures when the forces keeping the atoms in place are overcome.

Let us return to the experiments of Franck and Hertz, in which energy is transmitted to atoms by means of an electron beam. The threshold energy of a sodium atom—the minimum energy it is able to take in and add to its energy content—was found to be 2.1 electron volts, in the hydrogen atom it is as high as 10 electron volts. These are much higher energies than the energy of heat motion at room temperature. We immediately see a connection here with the fact that the atoms in a gas of room temperature maintain their identity and are not changed in spite of the many collisions they suffer. The energy of these collisions is 'way below the threshold energy, that is, below the smallest energy quantum that the atom can accept. Thus the Franck-Hertz experiments showed in their own way the surprising stability of atoms and gave it a quantitative aspect. The atom remains unchanged and stable so long as the impacts upon it are less energetic than a certain well-defined threshold energy, and this energy has a characteristic value for each element. Franck and Hertz "measured" the atomic stability.

The results of the Franck-Hertz experiments go farther than this. They tell us not only the minimum amount of energy which the atoms would accept; they tell us the whole series of specific energy values, from the minimum up, which the atom is willing to accept. Only these amounts of energy can be fed into the atom; it rejects anything in between. For example, the hydrogen atom accepts only the following amounts: 10 ev, 12 ev, 12.5 ev and 12.9 ev, and higher values at decreasing intervals. The sodium atom accepts only 2.1 ev, 3.18 ev, 3.6 ev, 3.75 ev, etc. Figure 24 shows a graphic representation of these energies. Each energy corresponds to a certain state of motion of the electron in the atom. Hence each line represents a selected state that the atom is allowed to assume. All other states lying in between are seemingly forbidden. The selected states are called quantum states. The state of lowest energy is the ground state in which the atom is found normally; the other ones are called excited states. The threshold energy is the difference between the energy of the first excited state and the ground state.

These facts contrast sharply with what we expect from the behavior of the planetary model. Why should the energy of the electrons be quantized within the atom? What prevents us from adding an arbitrarily small amount to the energy of an atom? If one compares the energy of an atom with the size of a bank account, it is as if the bank would allow only certain prescribed amounts of money to be withdrawn or deposited, to keep the value of the bank account at one of a series of predetermined numbers.

Let us now have a closer look at the different quantum states. One generally refers to the series of allowed energy values as the "spec-

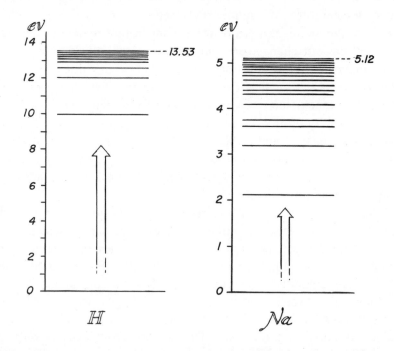

Figure 24. Energy of quantum states of hydrogen (H) and sodium (Na).

trum" of the atom. The two spectra in Figure 24 reveal a very important general property of quantum states. The higher the energy lies above the ground state, the smaller the energy gap between quantum states becomes. It is a property observed in all atomic systems; for large excitation energies the quantum states become so close to one another that they almost merge. At high energies the quantum effects disappear. The atom then is affected by any amount of energy, as an ordinary planetary system would be. It is as if the strange rules regarding the bank account are waived for very large accounts, since the permitted deposits and withdrawals become smaller and smaller for bigger accounts.

This fact has turned out to be of fundamental importance and much more sweeping than it appears here. Today we know that if we pumped great energy into atoms, they would behave as planetary systems do. These conditions can be realized under extremely high temperatures, which one can produce with strong electrical discharges in gases. Under these conditions the gas forms a so-called "plasma,"[2] and the atoms lose their characteric properties. A plasma of neon gas, where there are ten electrons per atom, has the same properties as a plasma of sodium gas, with eleven electrons per atom. There is no selected electron orbit any more; no one atom behaves like another; there is no characteristic radiation. Chaos reigns in a plasma; it is a chaos of very high temperatures and is rarely found here on Earth except when produced in our laboratories. We find it, however, in cosmic space among the gases expelled by the Sun and other hot stars.

In the plasma all orderly features disappear, the features by which we recognize one atom from the other. Order and differentiation occur only when the atoms are in their low-energy states, which are far apart on the energy scale. Then we find the stability that leads to specific shapes and orbits and, consequently, to specific chemical and physical properties. At high energy all these features are gone. Let us keep in mind, however, that it was the characteristic features at *low* energy that defied our understanding. The chaotic behavior of atoms at high energy is just what one would expect on the basis of a planetary model. It is just what one would expect of planetary systems colliding with one another at high speed.

---

[2] The name "plasma" has nothing to do with blood plasma, or the living matter in a cell. The first realizations of an atomic plasma in a discharge tube looked like the biological plasma; hence this terminology.

THE WAVE NATURE OF ATOMIC PARTICLES

Particle and Light Beams. We now come to the most striking but most revealing group of observations. They deal with the nature of the atomic particles. Let us consider the simplest form in which atomic particles, say electrons, are found. This is when they are removed from atoms, and freely moving in empty space. If all the electrons in a stream are all moving in the same direction and with the same speed, we call it an electron beam. Such beams are produced in any radio tube, in particular in television tubes. They hit the television screen from the inside of the tube and form the picture. Electron beams must be produced in a vacuum, since in ordinary air the electrons would bump into the air molecules and quickly get out of alignment.

You might expect that such electron beams would have very simple properties. They represent a group of particles moving along parallel trajectories at the same speed. They would travel in straight lines in free space; if they hit an obstacle, the particles would be scattered in all directions. On the contrary, however, we find very strange and unexpected phenomena.

Before we describe these effects, let us consider another kind of beam, a beam of light—the well-focused beam of a searchlight, for example. We assume that the light is of one color.

Let us compare these two beams. We expect them to be fundamentally different things: the light beam is a bundle of electromagnetic waves propagating through space in a certain direction; no material is moving, only the state of the electromagnetic field in space is changing. In contrast, a beam of particles should consist of actual matter in small units moving straight forward. You would expect the two to be as different as the motion of waves on a lake from that of a school of fish swimming in the same direction.

Let us recall the experiments in which we have shown the wave nature of light, in particular the setup in which an obstacle is put in the way of the beam, as indicated in Figure 14 of Chapter Three for light and in Figure 25 here for an electron beam. This setup seems to be ideal to bring out the difference between a beam of waves and a beam of particles. If the obstacle is put in the way of a particle beam, the particles that hit it will not get to the screen; the ones

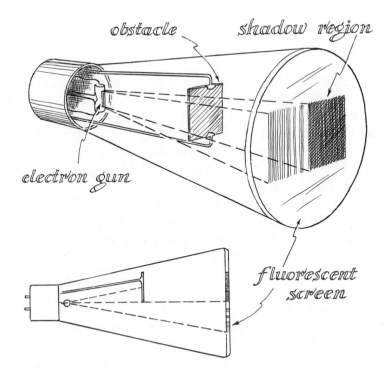

Figure 25. Electron-beam diffraction apparatus, analogous to light diffraction apparatus in Figure 14.

missing it will reach the screen; the ones just passing by at the edge might be scattered and deviated from their path. Hence, if we use a screen of the same material of which television screens are made, we should observe a region of shadow and a region of light, the transition being not quite sharp because of the scattering at the edge. No stripes are expected when no wave phenomenon is involved.

What a surprise for the physicists when they performed this and similar experiments and found electron beams exhibiting wave properties similar to those of light beams! Plate II shows the pattern an electron beam formed on a screen in the arrangement of Figure 14. The pattern is identical with the one of Plate IV observed with light. This amazing result is only one of many that have shown beyond doubt that electron beams must have some kind of wave nature; the propagation of a particle beam seems to have the character of a wave pattern. There must be a wave involved in the electron motion.

A quantitative study of these interference patterns allows one to measure the wave length of this mysterious "electron wave." The wave length depends upon the speed of the electron—the higher the speed, the smaller the wave length; for electrons with an energy of a few electron volts the wave length is of the size of the atoms. It is a very small wave length indeed, and this is why the wave nature of electron beams is not easy to detect. In most practical applications of electron beams, such as television tubes, the wave nature plays no role whatsoever.

Here a fundamental discovery was made—the wave nature of particles. The result is bewildering and highly unexpected. Many experiments had to be performed before the physicists were really convinced that the wave effects were not caused by some other phenomenon. All these experiments, however, only made it more and more clear that waves play a part in the motion of electrons and also of other atomic particles such as protons.

An obvious question poses itself: How can an electron be a particle and a wave at the same time? A wave is something that is spread over space in a continuous way, but a particle is strictly localized; at a given moment the particle is here and not there, whereas a wave is a state of "tension" of space that must spread over at least a few wave lengths in order to represent something that can be called a wave. Can we perform some decisive experiment to settle the question unambiguously? Is the electron really a particle or a wave?

This is perhaps the most interesting question of modern physics. But before we discuss this problem, we must be aware of the most exciting thing regarding the electron waves—the dual nature of electrons as particles and waves contains the clue to the riddle of atomic structure! The unexpected properties of the electrons circling around atomic nuclei are directly connected with their wave nature.

The Properties of Confined Waves. In order to understand the connections between electron waves and atomic properties, we must first study the peculiar behavior of waves when they are confined to a limited region.

Let us take the simplest example, of waves along an extended rope. If the rope is very long, we can produce a wave running along the rope by imparting to it a small impulse perpendicular to the rope, as every child playing with a skip rope knows well. If the rope is

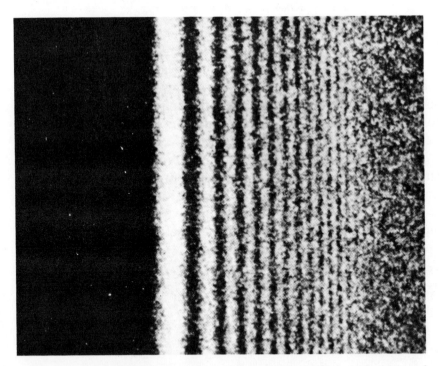

Plate IV. Interference of electrons is demonstrated by this actual photograph which is analogous to the phenomenon of Plate II.

tied at its far end to a fixed object and held under tension, the impulse travels along the rope and sometimes returns to us after being reflected at the point where the rope is attached. With adroit manipulation we can impart to the rope any form of wave, with long or short wave length, just as we wish. The long wave lengths will perform slow oscillations, and in the short ones the rope will vibrate fast when the wave passes by. Now let us confine the rope between two nearby points. It is then better to think not of a rope but of a string, which is suspended under tension between two points, such as a string on a violin. The form of vibration of such a string is what is called a *standing wave*. We have no longer the choice of wave length and frequency. In fact only those vibrations can be set up whose (half-) wave length fits once or twice or any integral number of times into the space between the two points of attachment, as shown in Figure 26.

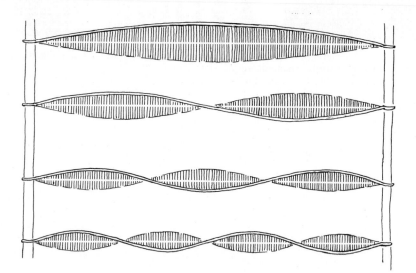

Figure 26. Standing waves. Vibrations of a string confined between the points of attachment. Only vibrations set up in which one, two, three, four, etc., half wave-lengths fit in the space between the attachments. Dotted line in position of the string at rest.

Not only the shapes of the vibrations are determined, but also the frequencies (the number of ups and downs per second), once the tension of the string is kept fixed. Each of the different vibrations which can be set up has its characteristic frequency, so the string can vibrate only with a set of given frequencies. The lowest of these frequencies, the easiest to set up, is the one whose half-wave length just fits the distance between the fixed ends of the string. It is the one the violinist plays when he sets the string in motion with his bow. But he can also set up higher vibrations, the so-called flageolet tones, where two or more half-wave lengths fit in the string.

Even when he plays a normal tone, the motion of the string is not purely the lowest vibration. The actual motion is a combination of several permitted forms of motion. In fact the ordinary musical tone of a violin contains the higher modes to a certain degree; they are the harmonics, whose presence is important for the beauty of the sound. The difference between the tone of Pablo Casals and that of an ordinary cello player is the different admixture of higher modes. But whatever the combination is, it can contain only frequencies from the set assigned to the tuned string.

The lesson learned with the string is true generally of all kinds of waves. Whenever waves are confined to a finite space, we observe special wave forms and a set of assigned frequencies which are characteristic of the system. Most musical instruments are built on this principle. The string instruments make use of the series of discrete and characteristic frequencies of the string. A wind instrument is based upon the assigned frequencies of air waves enclosed in the pipe of the instrument, be it a trumpet or an organ pipe.

Another interesting example of this phenomenon can be seen when water waves are confined, say, in a glass of water. You can observe a very striking example when you are riding in a propeller-driven airplane if you watch the water surface in a glass of water. Sometimes, when the frequency of the engine vibration is equal to one of the possible frequencies of the water waves confined in the glass, a special pattern of surface vibrations becomes visible. When the motor pitch changes or when the amount of water is changed, other patterns get into resonance with the motor pitch. You will be observing characteristic frequencies connected with characteristic wave patterns.

It would be perfectly possible to calculate the shape of these patterns and to predict at what frequency of vibration they are supposed to appear. All that one must know is the size and shape of the glass and the properties of waves on the water surface.

Electron Waves and Quantum States. Let us now return to the electron waves. How can one confine electron waves and observe similar phenomena? Any situation that confines electrons will also confine electron waves. Such a situation exists when an electron is close to an atomic nucleus. The positive charge of the nucleus attracts the electron and prevents it from leaving the immediate neighborhood of the nucleus; the electron is confined to a space near the nucleus. What effect will this confinement have on the electron wave? This question was asked and answered first by Erwin Schroedinger in 1926.

He was able to calculate the shape and the frequencies of the characteristic patterns that develop when electron waves are confined by a nucleus. It is a straightforward problem of dynamics of confined waves, once the relation between the wave length of the electron wave and the velocity of the electron is known. The result is a series of distinct vibrations, each of them with a characteristic pattern and frequency. The wave nature of the electron immediately "explains" the fact that the electron can assume only certain well-defined states of motion in the atom.

This result is of fundamental significance. A connection was found between the wave nature of the electron and the existence of discrete states in the atom. Here we are touching the very nerve of nature. When an electron is confined to a limited region around the nucleus, the wave properties of the electron permit only certain special, predetermined states of motion. Therefore the atom cannot change its state continuously; it must change abruptly from one allowed state to the other. It will stay in the state of lowest energy until it gets enough energy to be lifted into the next state, as it was observed in the Franck-Hertz experiment.

The success of the electron-wave picture of the atom is all the more remarkable because of the way it fits all facts in every quantitative detail. Schroedinger first calculated the simplest problem, the hydrogen atom, in which one single electron is confined by the nucleus. He found a series of states of vibration which correspond in every respect to the observed quantum states of the hydrogen atom. In particular, the frequencies of the electron-wave vibrations correspond exactly to the energies of the observed quantum states when the famous formula of Planck is used, which connects frequencies with energies: The corresponding energy E is always equal to the frequency ω (omega) multiplied by fixed number called *h:* $E=h\omega$. The number *h* is the so-called constant of Planck.[3] This relation is almost incredible to contemplate: Schroedinger calculated the vibrations of an electron wave confined by the attraction of

$$\mathcal{E}=h\omega$$

Figure 27. Planck's formula.

the center. He multiplied the frequencies by Planck's constant and obtained, exactly to the last decimal point, the energies of the quantum states of hydrogen, the allowed values of the energy bank account of the hydrogen atom.[4] Obviously the wave nature of the electron must be a decisive factor for the understanding of atomic properties.

The confinement of electron waves admits a series of possible states and furnishes a set of assigned frequencies. If we keep in mind the fundamental law connecting frequency with energy, we obtain a series of states with assigned energies. The one with the lowest frequency is the most important one, since it is the quantum state of lowest energy, the normal state of the atom. It is also the one that exhibits the wave nature most prominently.

The confined electron waves in atoms cannot be directly observed. We can measure their extension, their frequencies (to be exact, the differences between frequencies, which are observed as energy differences) and other indirect properties. But it is both constructive and impressive to look at pictures of these wave patterns. The pictures are not photographs; this would be impossible, as we shall see later in more detail. They are models made from the results of calculations. Plate V on page 99 shows the electron-wave patterns, in the order of increasing frequency or energy, of successive quantum states of an electron confined by a nucleus. The lowest state, the ground state, is the simplest one; the higher the frequency, the more involved is the pattern. The ground state has spherical symmetry. The next ones have a "figure-eight" form. The

[3] *h* is a very small number; if one measures energies in electron volts, and frequencies in ups and downs per second, $h=4\times10^{-15}$. A vibration of 10^{15} times per second corresponds to four electron volt.
[4] Everyone who contemplates this fantastic discovery sympathizes with the famous Italian physicist Enrico Fermi, who used to say when presenting this calculation in his lectures with his well-known Italian accent, "It has no business to fit so well!"

higher ones are usually more complex, although we also find simpler ones among them.

These patterns are of utmost importance in the make-up of nature. They are the fundamental forms on which matter is built. They are the shapes, and the *only* shapes, that the electron "motion" can assume under the conditions prevailing in atoms—that is, under the influence of a central force (the attraction of the nucleus) which keeps the electron confined. Hence these patterns are the symbols of the way in which nature combines and forms everything we see around us.

The patterns of Plate V and their inherent symmetries determine the behavior of the atoms; they are the basis of the orderly arrangement in molecules and also of the symmetric arrangement of atoms or molecules in crystals. The simple beauty of a crystal reflects on a larger scale the fundamental shapes of the atomic patterns. Ultimately all the regularities of form and structure that we see in nature, ranging from the hexagonal shape of a snowflake to the intricate symmetries of living forms in flowers and animals, are based upon the symmetries of these atomic patterns.

Looking at the patterns, we see that the higher we go in frequency (or energy), the finer the pattern becomes, the smaller are the distances between the ups and downs. The wave length becomes shorter. If one goes to very high frequencies (energies), the pattern is so varied and fine-grained that it looks almost smooth and continuous. Hence the motion it describes will be nearly the one of an ordinary particle without wave properties. Here again we see that our wave picture exactly reproduces what we have found in atoms. When the energy is high, the quantum phenomena cease to be important and the atom behaves as if it were an ordinary planetary system. The transition to the "plasma" conditions at high energy is also contained in the wave nature of the electron.

The hydrogen atom in its ground state vibrates in the simplest possible pattern, the first one in Plate V. Other atoms, however, exhibit the more complex patterns even in their ground states. This is explained by an important principle which was first discovered by Wolfgang Pauli in 1927. It says that when more than one electron is confined in an atom, each electron must assume a different pattern. Thus an added electron will have to assume the next higher pattern in the scale. The ground state of a complex atom is one of the excited states of a simpler atom.

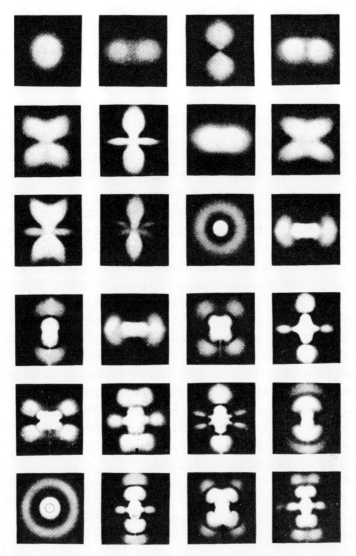

Plate V. These are photographs not of real electron patterns but of models carefully constructed according to our observations and calculations.

Here we find the explanation of the fact that one electron added or removed makes so much difference in the atomic world. The pattern of the last electron added determines the configuration of the atom. This in turn determines the way the atoms fit together, whether they form a crystal, a liquid, or a gas. This pattern can change appreciably when going from one number of electrons to the next higher one, as we can see from the examples in Plate V. Quantity becomes quality in the atomic world; one electron more may lead to a complete change of properties.

Schroedinger's discovery of the fundamental significance of the electron wave for the structure of the atom and the development of the theory by Heisenberg, Max Born, and Pauli mark a turning point in man's understanding of nature comparable to Newton's discovery of universal gravity, Maxwell's electromagnetic theory of light, and Einstein's relativity theory. The properties of the atoms, which seemed so strange and incomprehensible on the basis of the planetary model, fall into place when considered in the light of a confined-wave phenomenon. A confined wave assumes certain well-defined shapes and frequencies such as the vibration of the air in an organ pipe, of the string on the violin, or the water surface in a vibrating glass. They all form a series of vibrating patterns, beginning with the simplest pattern, which vibrates with the lowest frequency, and including more complicated patterns of higher frequencies. So do the vibrations of electron waves in atoms.

With this new way of looking at nature, we now can understand the three remarkable properties of the atom which we enumerated at the end of the last chapter. The *stability* comes from the fact that considerable energy must be added to change the lowest pattern to the next higher one.[5] As long as the effects upon the atom are less energetic than this energy, the atom remains in its lowest pattern. The configuration which it represents, therefore, exhibits the typical stability. The *identity* of atoms comes from the fact that the wave patterns are always the same and are determined by the way the waves are confined. One sodium atom is identical with another because the electron wave is confined in all sodium atoms by the same conditions—that is, by the attraction of the nucleus and the electric effects of the other electrons in the atom. The identity of two gold

[5] According to Planck's formula, this energy is equal to the frequency difference multiplied by Planck's constant.

atoms comes from the fact that the same number of electrons are confined by the same electric charge in the center and therefore produce the same wave vibrations. Finally, the ability to *regenerate* its original shape after distortion is exactly what one expects of a vibrational-wave phenomenon on the same grounds as the identity. When the original conditions are re-established, the electron vibration must assume again the same pattern as before, since the patterns are uniquely determined by the conditions in which the electron moves and are quite independent of what happened before. The patterns do not depend at all upon the previous history of the atom; we may destroy an atom by removing a few electrons or distort it by condensing the material into a solid, as we did in the example of sodium in the last chapter, but whenever we get the atom back into the original conditions, the electron waves will assume the same quantum states they had before. There exists only one wave pattern of lowest frequency or energy.

It is remarkable that we actually find in the world of atoms what Pythagoras and Kepler sought vainly to find in the motion of the planets. They believed that the earth and other planets move in special orbits, each unique to the planet and determined by some ultimate principle that is independent of the particular fate and past history of our planetary system. There is no such principle in the motion of planets, but there is in the motion of electrons in atoms—namely the wave principle. We are reminded of the Pythagorean harmony of the world: The atomic quantum states have specific shapes and frequencies that are uniquely predetermined. Every hydrogen atom in the world strikes the same chord of vibrations, as given by its set of characteristic frequencies. Here we find the "harmony of the spheres" reappearing in the atomic world, but this time clearly understood as a vibration phenomenon of confined electron waves. (See Figure 28.)

THE LIGHT QUANTA

The Graininess of Light. We have learned that electrons and other atomic particles exhibit wave properties. Particle beams sometimes behave as if they were waves. This property was shown to be the basis of the quantum behavior of the atoms. It turned out in the

Figure 28. Harmony of Spheres. (From HARMONICUS MUNDI by Johannes Kepler, 1619.)

course of research that this duality is not restricted to particles only. Light waves were found to behave sometimes as if they were particles.

All observations regarding the propagation of light indicate that a light beam is a continuous wave of oscillating electromagnetic fields. But when the effects of light upon matter were studied, some unexpected phenomena were observed that seemingly contradicted the picture of a continuous flow of light. What happens if light falls upon matter? If the object is transparent, such as a windowpane, light is partially reflected and partially transmitted. If the object is opaque, such as a piece of coal, or partially transparent, such as colored glass, a good part of the light is neither reflected nor is it transmitted. It disappears into the object. Since light is a form of energy, it can disappear only by giving its energy to matter in some way. This disappearance is called the absorption of light.

The energy of the absorbed light must show up in some other form. We feel the heat when sunlight is absorbed by our skin. When light is absorbed by some metals, its energy is often transferred to electrons, which then have acquired so much energy that they jump out of the metal. This jumping is called the photoelectric effect, which is of practical use when we want to transform light pulses into electrical pulses.

It is possible to measure with great accuracy the energy transferred to matter when light is absorbed. These measurements have had a most unexpected result: Light energy can be absorbed only in definite units of a certain amount; a fraction of these units can never be absorbed. If we compare energy with money, we might say that a light beam transmits its energy to matter only in full dollars but never in small change. The units are called light quanta, or photons. As far as the effect of light on matter is concerned, we can compare a light beam to a stream of bullets. Each bullet is filled with the same amount of explosive. Whenever a bullet hits an object, it causes an effect whose energy is determined by the amount of explosive. Stronger light means more explosions of the same size, but not stronger explosions.

In the photoelectric effect each light quantum hitting the metal forces an electron to jump out of the metal. The energy of the jumping electron is a measure of the size of the light quantum (it measures the amount of explosive in each bullet). The number of electrons jumping out measures the intensity of the light beam.

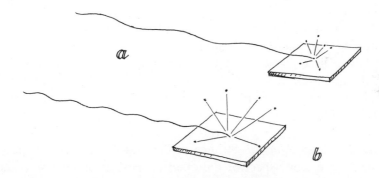

Figure 29. Photoelectric effect. (a) long wave length light impinging upon metal ejects slow electrons; (b) short wave length light ejects fast electrons.

The amount of energy in the light quantum depends upon the kind of light we are dealing with. It is different for light of different wave lengths—longer wave lengths have smaller units; shorter wave lengths, larger ones (Fig. 29.) The energy quantum of visible light is small. It contains an energy of only a few electron volts, about 10^{-12} (a millionth of a millionth) smaller than the energy necessary for a touch on your finger that you barely can feel. The quantum of radio waves (also a kind of light) is some billion times smaller, since their wave lengths are so much larger. Of course, the retinas in our eyes are much more sensitive to visible light than our finger tips. Still we would be unable to see single light quanta because they are too weak. If we could see them, a very weak light source would appear as an intermittent light, since we would see light only when a quantum arrived at the retina.

Although light is an electromagnetic wave, its effect on matter, on our eye, on the photoelectric cell, is quantized. It acts as if the light beam consisted of small grains, each of the same size. This phenomenon emphasizes the particle-wave duality in nature: Electrons are particles with wave properties; light is a wave with particle properties.

Let us be a little more quantitative. The size of the energy quantum of light is connected to the frequency of light by the same formula we already have encountered, the formula of Planck. The energy E of a quantum is given by $E=h\omega$, where ω is the frequency of light[6] and h is again Planck's constant. A quantum of visible yellow light ($\omega=5\times10^{14}$ vibrations per second) comes out to be about two electron volts.

Small as these quanta are, they are not small amounts of energy compared to the energies of atoms. They are of the same order of magnitude as the energy of the atomic quantum states. For example, the quantum of yellow light (two electron volts) is just equal to the energy necessary to lift the sodium atom from its ground state to its next higher state.

Atoms and Light Quanta. Strange as the idea of the light quantum is, it opens up a new aspect of the question how an atom limits and absorbs light, how light is produced by atoms, and how atoms are influenced by light. Let us combine the concept of the light quantum with the concept of the quantum states of the atom. We have learned that an atom can be found only in certain quantum states, with definite energies which are characteristic of the type of atom. Thus an atom can gain or lose energy only in amounts correspond-

---

[6] The frequency of a light wave is the number of vibrations of the electric field per second. Long wave lengths correspond to low frequencies; short wave lengths have high frequencies. Ordinary radio waves have frequencies of about 10^8 per second; visible light has frequencies of about 10^{16} per second.

ing to the energy differences between its quantum states. If the atom absorbs light or emits light, the energy of this light must be equal to one of those differences. Hence the atom can emit or absorb only light whose quanta have the correct amount—namely, an amount equal to one of these differences.

This property explains immediately why atoms radiate and absorb only light with certain typical frequencies. For example, an atom in its ground state can accept only light whose quantum energy is just the right size to lift the atom into one of the higher quantum states. An atom can absorb only light of those frequencies which possess the corresponding quanta. The same is true of light emission. Light can be emitted by an atom only when the atom is in a state higher than the ground state, and then it can emit only light whose quanta correspond to the energy difference between that state and a lower state. The atom can give off or take in only such light quanta that the energy balance will leave it again in a quantum state. Hence any light absorbed or emitted by an atom must have a frequency corresponding to the difference of two characteristic energy values.

Let us take the sodium atom as an example. When sodium gas is cool, all atoms are in the ground state. No radiation is emitted. The gas is transparent to light, except for light whose quanta would lift it to an excited state. For example, according to Figure 24 the first excited state is 2.1 ev higher than the ground state; hence light whose frequency is $\omega = \dfrac{2.1 \text{ ev}}{h} = 5.2 \times 10^{14}$ has the right quantum and will be absorbed by sodium gas. It is a special kind of yellow light. Let us now pour energy into the sodium gas either by heat or by an electric discharge, as is done in the yellow sodium street lights along some of our highways. Then a few sodium atoms will be put into higher quantum states. Those atoms are then able to emit light. The ones in the first excited state emit the same yellow light which the cool gas has absorbed. It is the color we see radiated by these street lights. When the temperature or the discharge energy is raised, higher and higher quantum states will be created and more colors will be radiated.

It is most remarkable how well the results of light-radiation experiments fitted the results of the Franck-Hertz experiments. Without exception, all frequencies emitted and absorbed by atoms correspond to a transition from one quantum state to another.

THE COMPLEMENTARITY BETWEEN THE PARTICLE AND WAVE PICTURES

Now we must return to our fundamental question: How can an electron be a particle and a wave at the same time? It is difficult to formulate the answer to this question in simple terms. The unexpected dual characteristic of matter has shown that our ordinary concepts of particle motion are not adequate for a description of what goes on in the atomic world. After all, these concepts are formed from human experience with visible objects which are larger than the atomic particles by factors of many billions. In order to understand what is going on at the atomic scale, we must be prepared to give up accustomed ways of thinking and replace them with new concepts that nature has forced upon us.

One of the features of classical physics that we must question is the "divisibility" of such phenomena. This is the idea that every physical process can be thought of as consisting of a succession of particular processes. According to this idea, theoretically at least, each process can be followed step by step in time and space. The orbit of an electron around the nucleus would be thought of as a succession of small displacements. Is this kind of description consistent with what one finds within the atoms?

In our ordinary way of looking at things, the electron must be either a particle or a wave. It cannot be both at the same time. After all, a careful tracing of the electron along its path must decide this question and put it in either one or the other category. Here the problem of the divisibility of atomic phenomena comes in. Can we really perform this tracing? There are technical problems in the way. If we want to "look" at the detailed structure of the orbit, we must use light waves with very small wave length, since one can see only things that are larger than the wave length of the light with which one observes. Such light, however, has a high frequency, hence a big energy quantum. In fact, light whose wave length is as small as an atomic orbit has quanta of an energy that would be far more than enough to tear away the electron from the atom. When it hits the electron, it will knock it out of its orbit and destroy the very object of our examination.

This reaction is not peculiar to experiments when light is used to trace the electron orbit. Quite generally, all measurements which could be used for a decision between the wave and the particle nature of the electron (or the proton, or any other entity) have the same property. If one performs these measurements, the object changes its state completely in the performance itself, and the result of the measurement applies not to the original state but to the state into which the object was put by the measurement. That latter state, however, is a state of very high energy which no longer shows any wave properties.

The quantum nature, the coarseness of light or of any other means of observation, makes it impossible to decide between wave and particle. It does not allow us to subdivide the atomic orbit into a succession of partial motions, be it particle displacements or wave oscillations. If we force a subdivision of the process and try to look more accurately at the wave in order to find out where the electron "really" is, we will find it there as a real particle, but we will have destroyed the subtle individuality of the quantum state. The wave nature will have disappeared, and with it all the characteristic properties of the atom. After all, it was the wave nature that gave rise to the typical properties of quantum states—the simple shape, the regeneration of the original form after perturbation, and all other specific qualities of the atom.

The wave nature of the electron is predicated upon the indivisibility of the quantum state. The great new insight of quantum physics is the recognition that the individual quantum states form an indivisible whole, which exists only as long as it is not attacked by penetrating means of observation. In the quantum state the electron is neither a particle nor a wave in the old senses. The quantum state is the form an electron assumes when it is left alone to adjust itself to the conditions at low energies. It forms a definite individual entity, whose pattern and shape correspond to a wave motion, with all the peculiar properties spreading out over a finite region of space. Any attempt to look at its detailed structure by direct observation would unavoidably destroy it, since the tools of observation would pour so much power into the system that the condition of low energy would no longer hold.

At this stage of our discussion it will appear quite natural that predictions of atomic phenomena sometimes must remain probability statements only. The prediction of the exact spot where the electron will be found after the quantum state has been destroyed with high-energy light is a case of this kind. If the quantum state is examined with pinpointing light, the electron will be found somewhere in the region of the wave, but the exact point cannot be predicted with accuracy. Only probability statements can be made—such, for example, as that the electron will be found most probably where the electron wave was most intense.[7]

Quantum mechanics has given us an unexpected but wonderful answer to a great dilemma. On the one hand, atoms are the smallest parts of matter; they are supposed to be indivisible and endowed with every detailed specific property of the substance. On the other hand, atoms are known to have an internal structure; they consist of electrons and nuclei, which necessarily must perform mechanical motions not unlike the planets around the Sun, and therefore cannot be imagined to exhibit the required properties.

The answer lies in the discovery of the quantum states which fulfill to some extent the first requirement. Their wavelike behavior endows them with the properties of identity, wholeness, and specificity, but the range of this behavior is limited. Only if they are exposed to perturbances smaller than a characteristic threshold will they retain their identity and their specific properties. If they are exposed to stronger perturbations, the atoms lose their typical quantum properties and exhibit the untypical behavior expected from the mechanical properties of its internal structure.

The quantum state cannot be described in terms of a mechanical model. It is a new state of matter, different from what we have experienced with large objects. It has a particular way of escaping ordinary observation because of the fact that such observation nec-

---

[7] The impossibility of measuring certain quantities relating to atomic particles is the basis of the famous uncertainty principle of Heisenberg. It states, for example, that one cannot determine with full accuracy both velocity and position of an electron. Clearly if one could, the electron would be recognized as a particle and not as a wave. The Heisenberg principle states that no measurement can be performed with sufficient accuracy to decide between the wave or the particle nature of the electron. This principle expresses a negative statement that certain measurements are impossible. We must recognize, however, the highly important fact that this impossibility of certain measurements is more than a mere technical limitation that some day might be overcome by clever instrumentation. If it were possible to perform such measurements, the coexistence of wave and particle properties in a single object would collapse, since these measurements would prove one of the two alternatives to be wrong. We know from a great wealth of observations that our objects exhibit both wave and particle properties. Hence the Heisenberg restrictions must have a deeper root: they are a necessary corollary to the duel nature of atomic objects. If they were broken, our interpretation of the wide field of atomic phenomena would be nothing but a web of errors, and its amazing success would be based upon accidental coincidence.

essarily will obliterate the conditions of its existence. The great Danish physicist Niels Bohr, who has contributed most to the clarification of these ideas, uses a special term for this remarkable situation; he calls it complementarity. The two descriptions of the atom—the wavelike quantum state on the one hand, and the planetary model on the other—are complementary descriptions, each equally true but applicable in different situations.

The quantum properties can unfold only when the atom is left undisturbed, or when it is exposed to perturbations which are less energetic than the quantum threshold. Then we find the atom with its characteristic symmetries, and it behaves like an indivisible entity. This is the case when we are dealing with matter under normal conditions. But when we try to look into the details of the quantum state by some sharp instrument of observation, we necessarily pour much energy into the atoms. Under these conditions the atoms behave as they would at very high temperature, that is as a plasma. We then observe the electrons as ordinary particles moving under the attractive force of the nuclei, without any quantum phenomena, and exactly as one would expect if one had to deal with ordinary old-fashioned particles.

Atomic phenomena present us with a much richer reality than we are accustomed to meeting in classical macroscopic physics. The wavelike properties of quantum states, the indivisibility of these states, the fact that we cannot describe the atom completely in terms of familiar things such as particles or classical waves, are features that do not occur with objects in our macroscopic experience. Hence the description of the atom cannot be as "detached" from the observing process as classical descriptions were. We can describe atomic reality only by telling truthfully what happens when we observe a phenomenon in different ways, although it may seem incredible to the uninitiated that the same electron can behave so differently as we observe it in the two complementary situations. These features, however, do not make electrons less real than anything else we observe in nature. Indeed the quantum states of the electron are the very basis of what we call reality around us.

CHEMISTRY

Chapter Six

THE CHEMICAL BOND

In the last chapter we examined the structure of the atom and saw how the wave pattern of the electrons endows each atom with its typical properties. We looked at each atom as a single unit by itself, but we did not consider what happens when several atoms come close to each other. We do know, however, that the smallest units of many materials are not atoms but molecules, which are groups of atoms, closely bound to each other. If we are to understand the structure of matter, we must understand not only the structure of atoms but also the reason atoms join and form molecules. We must understand what is called the chemical bond, which keeps the atoms together within the molecule, and we must get acquainted with a few typical molecules and their properties. The chemical bond and the properties of molecules are the subjects of chemistry.

Before the advent of quantum mechanics it was believed that there existed a special "chemical force" responsible for the chemical bond. It would have to be a most peculiar force, since some atoms stick together very well, others not at all. For example, once two hydrogen atoms and one oxygen atom have assembled into a unit, a molecule of water, no additional atom can be added to the group. The molecule is saturated; the chemical forces seem to have disappeared in respect to additional atoms.

Quantum mechanics has given a complete explanation of the chemical phenomena. There is no new force in action here at all. The chemical bond between atoms is the effect of the interplay of the electronic patterns of different atoms. A chemical bond arises when the patterns fit together well, like the cogs of the driving shafts in a gear or the pieces of a jigsaw puzzle. The patterns enmesh and interlace when the atoms are brought into contact; they merge into new wave patterns.

Some atomic patterns fit well together, others not so well. The chemical bond depends very much on the kinds of atoms involved. Sometimes they fit so well that, when a number of atoms are brought together, the patterns merge into one big round unit, not unlike the first picture in Figure 30, only somewhat larger and tighter. Then the assembly forms a saturated molecule, which will not bind any further atoms. A saturated molecule can be compared to a finished jigsaw puzzle, where all parts merge into one unit and there is no place for an additional part.

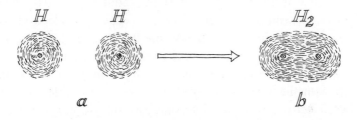

Figure 30. Two hydrogen atoms, each having the simplest electron pattern of Plate V, Chapter Five, form a hydrogen molecule where the two electrons merge into one elliptical pattern. The dots in the center are the hydrogen nuclei.

Since it comes from the combination and interlacing of electronic wave patterns, the chemical bond is fundamentally electric in its nature. Its strength is due to the quantum stability of the combined wave patterns in the molecule. A look at the various patterns of Plate V in the last chapter will make it easily understandable that there are many ways in which these patterns can be combined and enmeshed. Consequently we expect many different types of chemical compounds.

MOLECULES

Let us look at a few specific examples. Among the many ways atoms hold together there are two important kinds of bonds. One is the "twin-electron bond," and the other is "plug-and-hole" bond. A characteristic example of the first bond is the simplest molecule of all, the hydrogen molecule H_2, which consists only of two hydrogen atoms. Here the two electrons, one from each atom, merge into one pattern, and this merging keeps the atoms together (Figure 30). This merging seems to contradict Pauli's principle, mentioned on page 98, which says that not more than one electron can assume a given pattern. In fact, however, there is no contradiction; the electron has another interesting property which we shall mention here only in passing—it rotates around its own axis. This rotation is called the electron spin. Furthermore there are only two possible states of rotation, either to the left or to the right, about a given axis. Now any electron pattern must be counted twice, because an electron rotating either one way or the other can assume it. Hence two electrons, provided that they rotate in the opposite sense, can assume each pattern. This is why the electron spin plays such an important role in conjunction with the Pauli principle—it makes it possible for two, but only two, electrons to merge into one pattern. We can make a molecule out of two hydrogen atoms by having their electrons merge in a common pattern, but not out of three. The chemical binding is saturated with two electrons in one orbit.

A characteristic example of the plug-and-hole bond is the water molecule H_2O, which consists of two hydrogen atoms and one oxygen. The oxygen atom has eight electrons. Now it happens that ten electrons around an atomic nucleus form an assembly in a very tight, round pattern. The element *neon,* which has ten electrons, is chemically very inactive and does not form any molecules, but in the oxygen atom two electrons are missing from the tight pattern. Thus one can describe the pattern assembly of eight electrons as a tight round pattern with two holes in it. The holes have a well-defined shape, the shape of the missing electron pattern. In the case of oxygen the holes extend from the surface to the center, and the two holes are directed at right angles to each other (See Figure

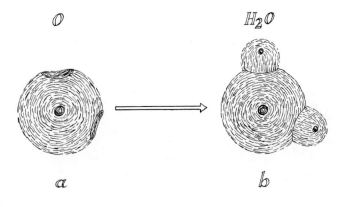

Figure 31. a. The oxygen atom. The electron pattern has two holes at right angles from the nucleus. b. The water molecule. The two holes in oxygen are plugged with hydrogen electrons. The hydrogen nuclei are within the hydrogen electron patterns (small black circles: hydrogen nuclei; large black circle: oxygen nucleus).

31a). Now we can understand the structure of the water molecule. The electrons of the two hydrogen atoms fit into the two holes; the hydrogen atoms act as plugs for these holes. Hence from the center of the oxygen atom the two hydrogen atoms should be separated by an angle of 90 degrees. The positive charges on the protons of the hydrogen atoms repel each other slightly and so increase the angle to slightly more than 90 degrees. It is in fact 108 degrees. (See Figure 31b.) This is a typical plug-and-hole bond.

Another interesting molecule-forming atom is nitrogen. It has seven electrons, of which four form a tight spherical pattern around the nucleus; the remaining three form a pattern of prongs extended in three directions perpendicular to each other—for example, forward, to the side, and upward (Figure 32a). With this picture we can easily understand the structure of the important molecule of ammonia NH_3, in which three hydrogen atoms form twin electron bonds with each of the prongs. The electrons of the hydrogen atoms merge with the electrons in the prongs, and we get a structure of the form indicated in Figure 32b, where the hydrogen nuclei sit at the tips of the nitrogen prongs.

The carbon atom is particularly suited for molecule formation. It has six electrons arranged as follows: Two of them are close to the nucleus in the form of a small round pattern. The other four can arrange themselves in a symmetric pattern in which each forms a radial

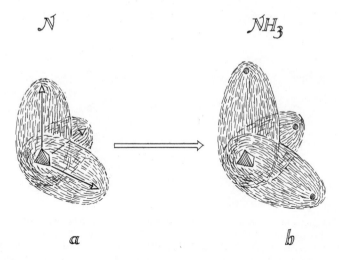

N   *NH₃*

a   *b*

Figure 32.   a. The nitrogen atom. There are three electron prongs in the directions of the arrows at right angles to each other. b. The ammonia molecule. Each electron prong of nitrogen merges with a hydrogen electron and forms an electron pair bond. The heavy triangle is the nitrogen nucleus. The small black circles are hydrogen nuclei.

prong away from the center. The tips of the four prongs form a regular tetrahedron (Figure 33a), and this picture enables us to understand the arrangement of the molecule of methane CH_4, which consists of one carbon atom and four hydrogens. Methane is the main component of cooking gas. The electrons of the hydrogen atoms merge with the four prong patterns in "twin-electron" bonds, creating a structure in which the carbon nucleus is in the center and four protons are at the corners of a tetrahedron (Figure 33b).

Another important molecule formed by carbon is carbon dioxide, which consists of one carbon atom and two oxygens. Here the four prongs are slightly bent; two go as plugs into the holes of one oxygen and the other two into the second oxygen. The result is a stretched structure with the carbon atom flanked by two oxygen atoms (Figure 34).

The carbon atom, with its four electron prongs, can form an unending series of molecules. The possibility of variety explains why carbon compounds are so common on earth and play a central rôle in living matter. Let us look at a few of these structures. The simplest is methane (Figure 35), with one hydrogen at each prong.

We also can build a molecule with two carbons and six hydrogens, as shown in Figure 35. Here all bonds are twin electron bonds. The molecule is called ethane. This principle can be continued as indicated in Figure 35, and we get a series of molecules called hydrocarbons: propane, with three carbons, butane, with four carbons, etc. The chainlike structures exist in any length desired. The short ones are gases, the longer ones liquids, and the very long ones, solids. They serve as burning fuel in the form of gas, oil, and candle wax, and we shall see later why they are well fitted for burning. The hydrocarbon chains are also important for our nutrition when they end up with a characteristic arrangement of atoms called the carboxyl group (Figure 36). Such chains are fatty acids and are the constituents of animal fat.

Other characteristic carbon structures are the alcohol molecules shown in Figure 37. Here the bonds toward the oxygen are plug-and-hole bonds.

Another important group of long-chain molecules are the carbohydrates. The chains are similar to the hydrocarbon chains, but there is an oxygen added to each step of the chain. The oxygen, as always, is tied on with plug-and-hole bonds. The simplest carbo-

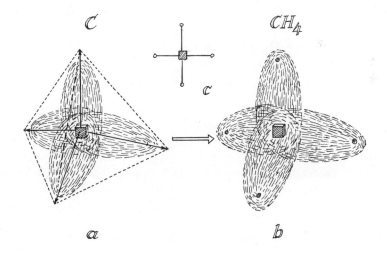

Figure 33. a. The carbon atom with its four electron prongs directed at the four corners of a regular tetrahedron. b. The methane molecule CH_4. Each electron prong of the carbon atom merges with a hydrogen electron and forms a twin electron bond. Dark square: carbon nucleus. Small circles: hydrogen nuclei. c. Schematic figure of CH_4. The twin electron bonds are indicated by lines.

CO_2

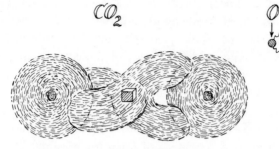

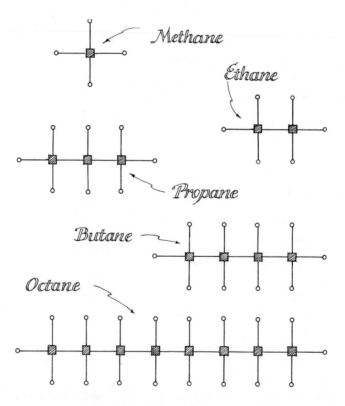

Figure 34. The carbon dioxide molecule CO_2. The four prongs of the carbon are plugging the holes of the two oxygen atoms. The schematic figure indicates the "plug and hole" bonds by wavy lines.

Methane

Ethane

Propane

Butane

Octane

Figure 35. Hydrocarbons. Schematic pictures of the molecules. Squares are carbon atoms. Small circles are hydrogen. Straight connecting lines are twin electron bonds.

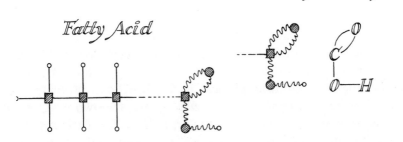

Carboxyl Group

Fatty Acid

Figure 36. Fatty acid molecule. A long hydrocarbon with a carboxyl group at the right end. The carboxyl group, COOH, consists of one carbon atom, two oxygens and one hydrogen bound together by plug and hole bonds. Squares are carbons; large circles oxygens; small circles hydrogens. Straight lines are twin electron bonds; wavy lines plug and hole bonds.

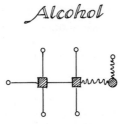

Alcohol

Figure 37. The alcohol molecule C_2H_5OH. Squares are carbons, large circles oxygen, small circles hydrogen; straight lines twin bonds, wavy lines plug and hole bonds.

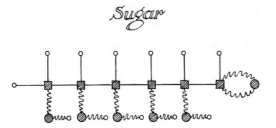

Sugar

Figure 38. Sugar. The glucose molecule $C_6H_{12}O_6$.

hydrate is glucose, which is a form of sugar (Figure 38). Cellulose is a very long carbohydrate. It is the material of which wood and other plant structures are made.

Next we come to a most important group of molecules, the amino acids. They are the building blocks of most living matter. Figure 39 shows the general principle of their structures. Carbon again, with its versatile four electron prongs, is the backbone of these molecules. The most characteristic, however, are the two end groups. At one end (on the right in the figure) there is a carboxyl group, and at the other end there is the amino group, NH_2. Between the two ends many different groups are found; each amino acid has its characteristic middle part. Figure 39 shows two of the simplest amino acids, glycine and alanine, and the general structure of the more complicated ones. The two end groups have a characteristic property. They can easily join. The amino group and the carboxyl group hang together (the so-called "peptide bond"), so that amino acids readily form long chains, one amino acid hitched onto the next. Such chains are called proteins; they play an important role in the functioning of life, as we shall learn in Chapter Eight.

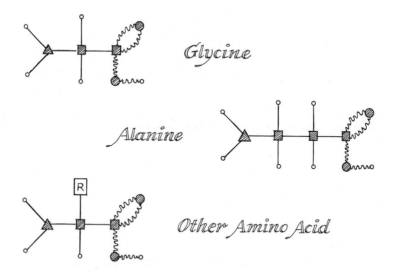

Figure 39. Amino acids. Amino acids have the carboxyl group at one end and the amino group NH_2 at the other end. The symbol R stands for various kinds of chemical compounds.

CHEMICAL ENERGY, CHEMICAL BURNING

So far we have given a descriptive account of a few of the most common molecules. Conditions in our environment on Earth are such that molecules are constantly formed and decomposed. If the Earth were much hotter, as on the surface of the Sun, molecules would never form because the thermal agitation is too strong—the atoms would not stay together. If it were much colder, the molecules would aggregate and form solids and crystals; no changes would occur. The temperatures on Earth are such that enough energy is available occasionally to break up some molecules but not too much energy, and most compounds can exist for some time. The making and breaking of molecules characterizes our environment, giving it the ever changing variety we see and establishing the conditions for the existence of life.

One of the most important consequences of formation of molecules is the release of energy. This release is most clearly seen when we burn coal or other substances. Every burning is connected with the formation of new molecules, and that is where the heat energy comes from. We must now see more clearly how and why energy is gained when atoms join to molecules. A chemical bond represents energy in the following sense: A certain amount of energy is needed

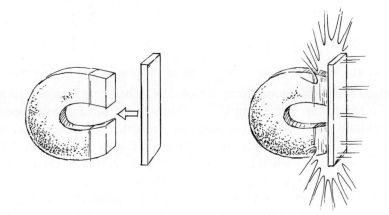

Figure 40. When the iron hits the magnet, the energy of magnetic attraction is transformed into heat and sound.

in order to break a bond; hence the same amount is gained if the bond is formed. As a simple example of a non-chemical bond, let us consider a magnet holding a piece of iron at its poles by magnetic attraction (Figure 40). It takes a certain amount of energy to remove the iron from the magnet. When the piece of iron is returned to the magnet, the same amount of energy is gained. The pull from the magnet has produced it. When we remove the iron from the magnet, our muscles supply the energy needed. Where does the energy appear which is produced when the piece is returned to the magnet? The energy appears partly in the form of sound, when the iron slaps on the magnet, and partly in form of heat—the iron is heated when it hits the magnet with force. The energy could even be used mechanically, if the piece of iron were rigged with strings and pulleys to have it perform work when attracted toward the magnet. (See Figure 41.)

Similar exchanges of energy occur in the case of the chemical bond. It takes energy to separate a molecule into atoms, and energy

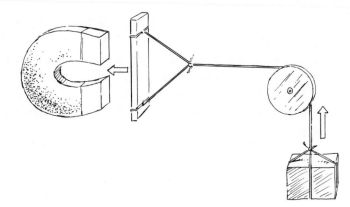

Figure 41.   In this arrangement the energy of attraction is used to lift a weight.

is gained when the atoms form a molecule. The energy gained turns up in many forms. For example, it appears in the form of vibrations: When atoms slap together, the molecule formed is set in vibration by the energetic encounter. Or in the form of energy of motion: The energy produced when the atoms collide and enmesh is then transferred to other neighboring molecules, whose motion is thereby accelerated. Altogether, whenever atoms form molecules, energy is released and usually turns up in the form of general motion, which is equivalent to heat.

There are some special cases in which the energy of bonding is not transformed into heat. The situation is analogous to the case where a piece of iron attracted by a magnet is rigged to have its motion perform useful work. Some chemical combinations can be arranged in such a way that the energy gained in molecule formation is transferred to another kind of molecule and raises the latter one into a new state of higher energy content. Then the energy of molecule formation is stored in this second molecule instead of being wasted in heat. This kind of rigging is important in the maintenance of life.

Some chemical bonds are strong, others are weak. When strong bonds are formed, larger amounts of energy are released. In general, plug-and-hole bonds are stronger than twin-electron bonds. It is harder to break off a hydrogen atom from a water molecule than from a methane molecule.

Let us consider in more detail a well-known chemical process, the burning of coal. What happens here? The carbon of the coal and the oxygen in the air form carbon dioxide. A piece of coal is an assembly of carbon atoms in a regular array, a carbon crystal. The oxygen in air does not exist in the form of isolated atoms, but in the form of oxygen molecules, which consist of two oxygen atoms bound together by twin-electron bonds. Hence the chemical reaction of coal burning is

$$C + O_2 = CO_2$$

Figure 42.

The reaction must proceed in two stages: First the O_2 bond must be split; second the two O atoms must be attached to the carbon: The first stage needs energy. It does not proceed with energy provided at ordinary temperature. After all, a piece of coal can be in contact with air without burning. The heat energy at normal temperature is not high enough to split the oxygen molecule into two atoms. But if we provide heat from the outside in the form of a lighted match or kindling wood, the reaction starts. We need only to provide heat for the starting of the process because the second stage, the formation of CO_2, supplies more energy than required for the splitting of O_2. The former is a plug-and-hole bond and the latter a twin-electron one. The energy for the subsequent splittings of O_2 is provided by the process itself. The burning of coal therefore

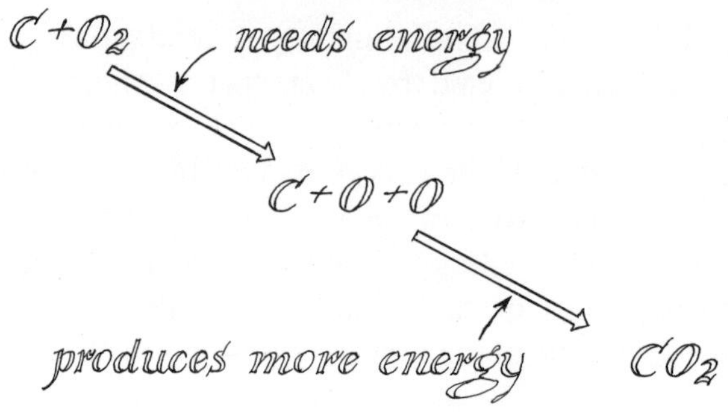

$$C + O_2 \quad \text{needs energy}$$

$$C + O + O$$

$$\text{produces more energy} \qquad CO_2$$

Figure 43.

produces energy in the form of heat even though part of the energy produced in the second stage must be used to initiate further reactions. The useful heat is the surplus of the energy in the second stage over the energy needed in the first.

Once started, the production of carbon dioxide proceeds until all carbon is used up. Intense heat is produced; there is a net energy gain of 0.67 ev per each carbon-dioxide molecule formed. The heat is so great that it causes atoms and molecules to emit light. The flames we see leaping up from the coal are molecules of CO_2 and carbon atoms ejected by the intense heat and made to radiate in their characteristic light. Fire, therefore, is not a new form of matter, as people once believed; it is the incandescent material produced in a chemical reaction which develops a large amount of energy.

The burning of coal is the simplest form of chemical energy production. A similar process occurs in the burning of methane or any other hydrocarbon. Here again the initial heat is necessary in order to split not only the O_2 molecules in air, but also the hydrocarbon molecule. Then the carbon combines with oxygen to form carbon dioxide, and the hydrogen combines with oxygen to form water. The chemical reaction for the burning of the methane is shown in Figure 44.

Since both CH_4 and O_2 are twin-electron bonds, and both CO_2 and H_2O are plug-and-hole ones, we get a large net energy yield in this reaction. Therefore methane and the other hydrocarbons burn in air with intense flame and heat. In contrast to carbon burning, however, not only CO_2 is produced, but also water. The flame contains not only incandescent CO_2 gas, but also water vapor. If you hold a cold piece of glass in a candle or wood flame, you will find

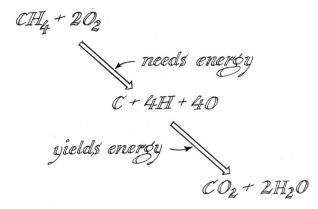

$$CH_4 + 2O_2$$

← *needs energy*

$$C + 4H + 4O$$

yields energy →

$$CO_2 + 2H_2O$$

Figure 44.

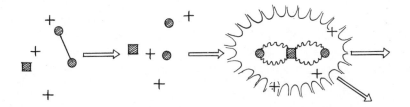

Figure 45. The burning of carbon. In the first figure we see one carbon atom (square), one oxygen molecule (two circles bound by a twin electron bond), and three other molecules or atoms symbolized by the crosses. In the second figure the heat motion of the "cross" molecules has torn the bond of the oxygen molecule. In the third picture the carbon and the two oxygen atoms have joined to a CO_2 molecule. The energy released goes partly into more heat energy of the "cross" molecules, and partly into vibrations of the CO_2 molecule as indicated by the "halo."

condensed water vapor on it, but you will not if the flame is from pure coal.

In the same way any other molecule built up from carbon, hydrogen, and oxygen can burn—that is, if it is transformed into carbon dioxide and water with the help of oxygen in the air. Molecules such as alcohol or sugar need less atmospheric oxygen for burning, since they already contain some oxygen.

Chemical reactions that produce energy must always start with molecules with weak bonds and end with molecules with very strong bonds. The difference of the weak and strong bond strengths is released as energy. CO₂ and water are molecules with strong bonds, and so are most molecules where atoms are bound to oxygen. Molecules containing carbon and hydrogen, however, are loosely bound; they are easily broken and recombined, they can form long chains, and are apt to assemble in complicated structures. Transformed into stronger bonds with oxygen in a complex process, they yield energy. Because of these properties they play an important role as the constituents of living matter.

THE STATES OF AGGREGATION

The chemical bond keeps the atoms tied within the molecules. Are there also forces between the molecules? Such forces do exist, indeed, but they are weaker than the chemical bond. When two molecules come near each other, the electron patterns in each unit have a tendency to vibrate in unison. This tendency produces an attraction (the so-called van der Waals force). Its strength depends upon the nature of the electron motion—some molecules attract each other strongly, others only very weakly. This intermolecular force is another characteristic feature based upon the special properties of the electron patterns.

The intermolecular force keeps one molecule close to another, and therefore is responsible for the aggregation of molecules as we find them in liquids and solids. The molecules stick together, but in gases each molecule moves by itself. Why do molecules sometimes aggregate as solids, sometimes as liquids, and sometimes, when they form gases, not at all? The state of aggregation depends strongly on the temperature. At very low temperature almost all substances become solid, at very high temperature all substances are gases, and they all are liquid at some intermediate temperature. The values of the temperatures (melting point, boiling point) at which these transitions occur differ for different substances, and these values depend upon the strength of the attraction between molecules.

At very low temperature there is very little heat motion, and therefore the molecules can arrange themselves neatly in regular arrays and are kept in these patterns by the intermolecular forces. They form a solid. The regular arrangement of the molecules is often beautifully displayed in crystals. We have seen in Chapter Four how the field-ion microscope displays such a regular pattern in tungsten. Crystals are solids in which the ordered pattern is maintained over a large volume and becomes directly visible in the straight edges and geometrically arranged planes and points. Since they multiply the tiny order by an enormous factor, crystals give us a direct picture of the symmetry of the smallest units. If you try to deform a solid by bending or breaking, you feel a resistance—you are changing the arrangement of the molecules and must overcome the intermolecular forces which keep the molecules in the regular pattern.

The molecules and atoms are so close in solids that they often merge into each other; neighboring electron patterns sometimes overlap so much that the whole solid material should be considered as one big molecule. It is characteristic of metals, for example, that the outer electrons of the atoms move in a pattern which is spread over the whole metal. Hence metals are good conductors of electricity; the electrons move freely from one atom to the next.

At higher temperatures the irregular heat motion becomes stronger and destroys the ordered arrangement of molecules or atoms in solids. Still the intermolecular forces keep the molecules tightly packed adjacent to each other, but they no longer can force them into a regular array. Hence there will be no resistance to deforming or bending. But the molecules will still stay together: they form a liquid. The transition from the solid to the liquid depends on the strength of the intermolecular forces. If they are strong, as in rock or metal, it will take a high temperature to overcome the bonds that keep the molecules in the regular pattern; if they are weak as in water or air, the transition occurs at lower temperature.

If the temperature rises still higher than the melting point, the heat motion becomes stronger, until it can overcome not only the ordering effect but also the packing effect of the forces. Then the molecules torn from each other by the heat motion fly off in all directions, colliding with other molecules and hitting the walls of the container. They no longer are tightly packed, but are spread over the whole volume available. They form a gas. The point at which a gas is formed depends again on the strength of the intermolecular forces. In air the forces are so weak that they cannot keep the molecules together even at ordinary temperatures. In some metals and rocks the forces are so strong that about 4000° Fahrenheit is needed to produce gaseous state.

The increase of temperature reduces the specific properties and the organization of the substances. In the solid state substances exhibit typical forms as crystals, have a specific texture and hardness, and are easily identifiable. In the liquid state shape and texture are gone—the substance assumes the form of the container. Only a characteristic density, color, and surface remain. This transition is displayed dramatically when a snowflake, with all its intricate hexagonal structure, melts into a shapeless drop of water. The gaseous state has even less specificity. There is no characteristic density any more, no surface, nothing but a shade of color and smell. Still, in all three states the substance consists of the same molecules or atoms; the same metal atoms form solid or liquid metal or gaseous metal vapor; the same water molecules form ice, water and steam.

THE QUANTUM LADDER

Chapter Seven

SIZE AND STABILITY

We have seen in the previous chapter that everything that we see around us is a combination of ninety-two atomic nuclei and their electrons. The substances and the shapes of all things are the result of an interplay of various electron patterns and their combinations. Electrons assume their characteristic wave patterns when they assemble around the atomic nuclei; they form atoms and the atoms join into molecules. These patterns are responsible for the specific properties of all materials and give each substance its special character.

The patterns can be deformed and destroyed in energetic collisions or other strong perturbations, but they exhibit a certain typical stability. We have seen, for example, that at the temperatures we experience here on the Earth's surface the heat motion is not energetic enough to destroy atomic and most molecular patterns. This is the reason the substances we find in our immediate surroundings have specific properties. The limit of stability of an atom or molecule is different for the various types of atoms and molecules. It depends on many factors, but mainly on the size. Large units have lower stability than small ones. Big molecules can be broken up more easily than small ones. The extremely large molecules that make up organic material such as meat or vegetables, for example, are broken into pieces in the process of digestion, which goes on at a relatively low temperature in our stomach. But as we saw in the last chapter, the breakup of the much smaller oxygen molecule needs the temperature of a flame. The removal of an electron from a hydrogen atom, the smallest of all atoms, needs even higher energies. It cannot be done in a flame, but only in a strong electric discharge.

The relation between size and stability is a direct consequence of the wave nature of particles. Let us remember the fact that a long piano string gives a lower pitch and lower overtones than a short string does. In close analogy, a large wave pattern would have lower frequencies too. According to our fundamental frequency-energy relation, lower frequency means lower energy. We expect a wave pattern of large size to possess less energy and also to be sensitive to perturbations of lower energy. This is why the size-stability relation has such general validity. The smaller the system, the higher will be its stability, the more energy needed to change its characteristic structure.

THE STRUCTURE OF NUCLEI

As we have seen, matter consists of electrons and atomic nuclei. Each element has its own atomic nucleus, which carries a charge of a certain number of units. This charge is responsible for the character of the atom, since it determines the number of electrons in the atom and therefore the patterns which the electrons assume. At this stage of our story the nucleus of an atom is an indivisible entity, whose charge and mass are characteristic of each type of atom. Each element has its own typical nucleus. Matter is made up of many different "elementary particles": the electrons and the various atomic nuclei, a different one for each element.

But this is not a satisfactory state of affairs. One would prefer to think that the various types of atomic nuclei are all combinations of a few simple constituents. Any nucleus would be a structure made up of these constituents, and they, the constituents, would be the elementary particles, rather than the nuclei.

So far we have considered the atomic nuclei as massive particles, endowed with a positive charge but seemingly without any internal structure. Could it be that their lack of structure is apparent only, just as atoms below their excitation threshold seem also to lack structure? The small size of the nucleus would indicate a very high threshold according to our size-stability relation, very much higher than the corresponding energies in atoms. Perhaps we should expect that the internal structure of the nucleus would be of no importance in the dynamics of atoms, and would be observed only when much higher energies came into play than those with which we deal in atomic or molecular problems.

It was one of the most remarkable developments in modern physics when experiments revealed the same kind of quantum world within the tiny nucleus as we have found in the much larger atom. It turned out that the atomic nuclei indeed have a structure, and that they are made of two kinds of particles, protons and neutrons. The proton is identical with the lightest atomic nucleus, the nucleus of the hydrogen atom; it carries one unit of positive charge, and its mass is 1860 times heavier than the electron. The neutron is a particle of almost exactly the same mass as the proton but without any charge.

The remarkable thing is that these particles also exhibit wave features similar to those of the electrons. It is true that the wave properties depend on the mass of the moving particle; the heavier it is, the shorter is the wave length and the harder it is to observe wave effects. Still, the wave effects give rise to characteristic wave patterns as soon as the motion of the particles is confined. There is a force within the nucleus that keeps the protons and neutrons together; it is the nuclear force acting between the protons and neutrons, and it confines the particles within the volume of the nucleus. The confining effect of this force produces patterns of proton and neutron waves, similar to the electron patterns in atoms.

We find the same quantum effects repeated again within the nucleus that we have observed in the atom. Quantum states, stability thresholds, characteristic patterns, identity of nuclei of the same type, all are observed again on a much smaller scale in size, but, because of the size-energy relation, on a much larger scale in energy.

In order to find out about the structure of the atomic nuclei one must overcome the threshold energies of the nuclear quantum states. These energies were found to be as high as a hundred thousand to a million electron volts. Energies of this amount are hard to get at. The first experiments of "smashing" an atomic nucleus were made with alpha particles, which are ejected with very high energy from certain radioactive substances. These are the same particles with which Rutherford discovered the existence of the atomic nucleus in 1911.

Only a few years later, in 1919, Rutherford again used alpha particles for another fundamental discovery. When he directed alpha particles into nitrogen gas, he found that the bombardment could break the nitrogen nucleus into pieces. He was able to show that a *proton* was broken off from the nitrogen nucleus, and thus he proved that nuclei contain protons as constituents.

Since this memorable date an enormous amount of knowledge has been accumulated in regard to the structure of atomic nuclei. After 1930 machines were invented and constructed to accelerate protons or alpha particles artificially to very high energies, and we no longer need to use radioactive rays for the investigation of atomic nuclei. These machines have different names: cyclotrons, synchrotrons, electrostatic accelerators, etc.; popularly they are called "atom smashers," but they should be called "atomic nucleus smashers." The atom is easily taken apart by heat or electrical discharges. When we light a match, we take atoms apart; many atoms in the tip of the match lose one of their electrons in the little explosion that occurs. It is the atomic nucleus, not the atom, that resists any interference with the structure until one reaches energies of millions of electron volts.

In some ways, however, the word "atom smasher" is apt. The atomic nucleus is not only the center of the atom, it is the essential part. Almost all the mass of the atom resides in the nucleus. The surrounding electrons weigh less than $1/2000$ of the total mass. More than that, the electrons can be removed and replaced. It is the charge of the nucleus that determines the pattern in which the electrons surround the nucleus, and the pattern that determines the properties of the atom. The nucleus is the part that characterizes the atom with its special properties. When Rutherford and his collaborators for the first time changed one atomic nucleus into another (they broke off a proton from a nitrogen nucleus, reducing its charge by one unit, thus making it into a boron nucleus), they fulfilled the great dream of the alchemists, the transmutation of one element into a different one. (See Figure 46.)

In our study of the structure of the nucleus we have hit upon a new force of nature, the nuclear force, the force that keeps neutrons and protons tightly bound within the confines of the nucleus. It is a very strong force; it not only must overcome the electric repulsion between the positively charged protons, but also confines many particles within an extremely small spatial area.

Figure 46. Old Alchemist drawing. From Philip Ulstadt's *De Secretis Naturae,* 1544.

The discovery of this force was an important step in our insight into the workings of nature. Up to that point only two types of forces had been found in nature, the force of gravity and the electromagnetic forces. The force of gravity governs the motion of large units of matter, the motion of heavenly bodies and the falling motion of objects on earth. Gravity is much too weak on an atomic scale and therefore does not play any rôle within atoms and molecules. It was the great achievement of quantum mechanics to show that the properties of matter, the structure of atoms and molecules, can all be explained on the basis of electric attraction between the atomic nuclei and the electrons in the atom, and on the electron patterns formed under the influence of the electric attraction. Now in our study of the structure of the nucleus we have hit upon a new force of nature, the nuclear force. We have no direct human experience of this force, such as we have of the other two forces. Everybody has felt the force of gravity on a heavy object, and has seen the effect of electric or magnetic forces. Gravity and electricity have an infinite range. The effect of gravitational and electric attraction decreases with increasing distance in accordance with the well-known inverse square law, but it is noticeable at any distance. The nuclear forces are much harder to detect, mainly because of their very short range. Nuclear forces break off completely at very short distances. They have been found to act over stretches of only 10^{-13} centimeters, a length which is 100,000 times smaller than the size of an atom. Of course it is impossible to notice directly the effect of nuclear forces on an ordinary human scale.

Indirectly the nuclear forces play an enormous role: if these forces did not exist, the nucleons (nuclear particles) would fly apart from one another. Without them there would be no atomic nucleus, except a proton; hence there would be no atoms except hydrogen. Furthermore, as we shall see later, the solar energy supplying us with heat and power comes ultimately from the effects of nuclear forces, and recently man was able to use and abuse the effects of nuclear fission which are a direct consequence of nuclear forces.

Nuclear physics proceeded along the same lines as atomic physics. In the 1930s, only ten years after the discovery of the wave nature of atomic electrons, specific quantum states were found within the nucleus. It was established that the light which nuclei emit and absorb has characteristic frequencies corresponding exactly to the

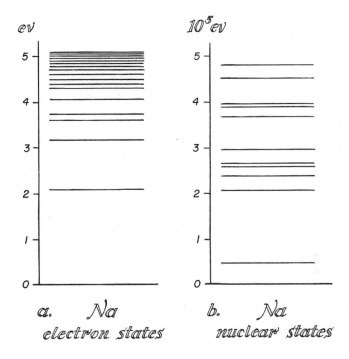

Figure 47. The quantum states of the sodium electrons (a) compared with the quantum states of the sodium nucleus (b). The states (a) are the same as in Figure 24, Chapter Five. Note that the scale of (b) is 100,000 times larger.

differences of energy between two nuclear quantum states. (See Figure 47.) When changing from a higher energetic quantum state to a lower one, the nucleus, as well as the atom, releases the energy difference in the form of a light quantum whose frequency ω corresponds to the energy difference E according to Planck's formula $E=h\omega$. The difference lies in the amount of the energies involved. When changing from one quantum state to another, atoms usually emit visible light; atomic nuclei emit light of much higher frequency because the energy differences are more than a hundred thousand times larger. This light is like very penetrating X rays, and it is referred to as "gamma rays."

There is also another difference between the quantum mechanics of atoms and of atomic nuclei. In the atomic case we know exactly the nature of the force confining the electrons to the nucleus; it is the electrostatic attraction. It is possible to calculate the electron wave patterns and to predict accurately the energy and shape of the quantum states. In the case of the atomic nucleus the confining force is new to us and unknown. We cannot calculate the wave patterns as well as we wished. All we can do at present is to try to determine the properties of the new force by studying the observed wave patterns. You can appreciate the difficulty when you consider that atomic nuclei are ten thousand times smaller than atoms. Still, a considerable knowledge has been accumulated regarding the new force. We know at present its range, its size, and some of its detailed properties, including one remarkable fact: Although attractive over most of its range, the force turns repulsive if the nucleons come very close to each other.

Nuclear physics has taught us one outstanding lesson. All matter consists of three types of elementary particles—protons, neutrons, and electrons. Everything in nature is a combination of these three entities. Protons and neutrons combine to form atomic nuclei; electrons fall into their patterns around the nucleus and form the atom; atoms combine into molecules and molecules aggregate into matter as we see it around us. A great step has been achieved by this reduction of the variety of substances to only three elementary units, whose various combinations under the influence of nuclear and electromagnetic forces make up all the materials of the universe.

ISOTOPES, RADIOACTIVITY

An atomic nucleus is composed of neutrons and protons held together by the nuclear forces. The proton is charged, the neutron is not; hence the charge of the nucleus is determined by the number of protons. This charge is an important quantity, since it determines the kind of atom which will be formed around the nucleus, and therefore it characterizes the element to which the nucleus belongs. The neutrons serve only as a glue; they help to keep the protons together.

The nuclear forces act most efficiently when the number of neutrons is about equal to or slightly larger than the number of protons. This is the arrangement we find in most of the nuclei. For example, the helium nucleus (charge: two units) consists of two protons and two neutrons; the carbon nucleus has six protons and six neutrons; nitrogen has seven protons and seven neutrons.

Sometimes a certain number of protons form nuclei with different numbers of neutrons. The different nuclei are of the same element (the element is determined by the number of protons) but of different weight. Two such samples of the same element will differ only in the number of neutrons in their nuclei and hence in atomic weight, and are called isotopes. For example, a carbon nucleus with six protons and seven neutrons, an isotope of the ordinary carbon, exists, and there is a nitrogen nucleus with seven protons and eight neutrons, an isotope of the ordinary nitrogen. We denote the two carbon isotopes with the symbols C^{12} and C^{13} and the two nitrogen isotopes with N^{14} and N^{15}. The number indicates the total number of constituents, neutrons and protons together. The isotopes C^{13} and N^{15} are much rarer than the ordinary types of C^{12} and N^{14}.

Why can one not put more neutrons, say eight, or fewer, say five, neutrons together with six protons into a carbon nucleus? One then would get carbon isotopes with a total number of fourteen or eleven; C^{14} and C^{11}. This is indeed possible; C^{11} and C^{14} can be formed by suitable application of accelerator machines. But such nuclei, with an abnormal surplus of one kind of particle, exhibit a strange phenomenon.

This phenomenon, which occurs whenever the number of neutrons gets much out of balance with the number of protons, is called radioactivity. Slowly but surely, a proton transforms itself into a neutron when there are too many protons, as in C^{11}; or a neutron changes into a proton if there is an abnormal surplus of neutrons, as in C^{14}. Then C^{11} becomes a nucleus with six neutrons and five protons, and that is a boron nucleus, B^{11}; C^{14} transforms into a nucleus with seven protons and seven neutrons, and that is a nitrogen nucleus, N^{14}. (See Figure 48.)

This transformation process is of special interest. It occurs steadily and slowly with a fixed half life, which is twenty minutes in the case of C^{11} and 4700 years in the case of C^{14}. We use the term "half life" because after twenty minutes half of the C^{11} nuclei become B^{11} nuclei; after another twenty minutes half of the remaining C^{11} is transformed, etc. The same regular process occurs with C^{14} in steps of 4700 years.

Each transformation is accompanied by the emission of particles. After all, the electric charge cannot suddenly change from six to five units, or from six to seven, without having other changes occur.

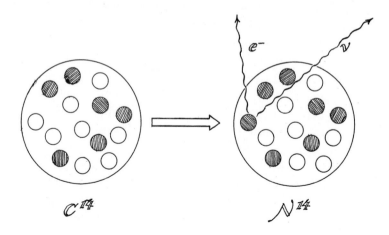

Figure 48. Radioactive transformation of carbon fourteen to nitrogen fourteen. One neutron changes into a proton and emits a negative electro (e⁻) and a neutrino (ν.). Open circles are neutrons, dark protons.

The nucleus must adjust in some way to the difference in charge. Two particles are emitted; one is an electron, positive[1] or negative, the other a "neutrino." The neutrino, which is the uncharged counterpart of the electron, is very light—in fact, it has zero mass. Because it carries no charge and therefore is not subject to electrical attraction or repulsion, it penetrates matter very easily. The emitted electron is a positive one if a proton changes into a neutron as in C^{11}; it is a negative one when a neutron transforms into a proton as in C^{14}. Hence the changes of charge are compensated for.

The two particles are emitted with considerable energy. In the $C^{11} \rightarrow B^{11}$ transformation the electron-neutrino pair gets about 1 million electron volts; in the $C^{14} \rightarrow N^{14}$ case it gets 15000 electron volts. These energies are set free because the end products (B^{11} or N^{14}) have a lower energy than the initial nuclei. As we saw in the last chapter, a transition from a loosely bound system to a more tightly bound one always gives rise to a surplus energy. B^{11} and N^{14} have a more balanced neutron-proton ratio than the initial nuclei and therefore are more tightly bound.

Radioactive nuclei are of considerable importance in medicine

[1] So far we have heard only of negative electrons. All electrons in atoms are negative. Positive electrons do exist, however, but they have a most interesting property: Whenever a positive electron hits a negative one, they annihilate each other, and their combined mass is transformed into light energy. They disappear with an explosion. A positive electron is the so-called "anti-particle" to the electron.

because the energetic electrons affect living tissues. There are many other practical applications of radioactivity besides the medical ones. With modern accelerators it is relatively easy to produce radioactive nuclei. To obtain nuclei with an abnormal surplus of protons or neutrons, we only have to bombard ordinary nuclei with protons or neutrons. Some of these radioactive isotopes have half lives of a few seconds, some have a few hours or years; a few have half lives of billions of years. These long-lived ones need not be produced artificially; they are found on the surface of the Earth, radium being a well-known example. They were produced at a time when the material of the Earth was subjected to natural bombardment by protons or neutrons, 'way in the past in some big star explosion. Because of their long half life, they are still with us.

Radioactivity[2] is a change from an unbalanced nucleus to a more stable one of different charge, accompanied by an emission of electrons and neutrinos. The process is puzzling; we do not know its significance or its relation to other nuclear phenomena. It is a very slow process. Years, hours, even seconds are very long periods of time from the point of view of a nuclear system, where motions are extremely rapid. Rutherford once said radioactive transformations are so slow that they practically do not occur at all! But still they do exist. Even a solitary free neutron lives only ten minutes when it is not built into a nucleus. It transforms itself spontaneously into the more stable proton with simultaneous emission of an electron and a neutrino. As part of a non-radioactive nucleus, however, a neutron is as stable as a proton.

NUCLEAR ENERGY, NUCLEAR BURNING

The heat of burning coal comes from the union of carbon and oxygen atoms, forming a molecule in which they are strongly bound to each other. Energy is created whenever atoms join together and form a strongly bound unit. Can we apply the same principle to the

---

[2] The term "radioactivity" includes another phenomenon which has nothing to do with the one we have described. Some heavy nuclei, such as uranium or thorium, are slightly unstable and, after very long time periods, decay by expelling an energetic alpha particle. This particle is identical with the helium nucleus. Rutherford used this kind of radioactivity for his experiments with alpha particle beams. Before the invention of accelerators, this was the only source available for high-energy particle beams.

bonds within the nucleus? Energy should be produced when neutrons and protons get together and form a nucleus. A nuclear fire should exist and should be much more powerful than any ordinary fire, since the energies involved in nuclear phenomena are a hundred thousand times greater than the energies occurring in the electronic orbits of the atoms.

Let us consider a simple example of nuclear burning. The nucleus of helium consists of two protons and two neutrons, which are bound together by nuclear forces. The nucleus of carbon consists of six protons and six neutrons bound together tightly; hence we can think of carbon as being three helium nuclei in close bond. If one could press three helium nuclei into close contact so that the nuclear forces began to act between them, they would snap together, forming a carbon nucleus and releasing large amounts of energy. Helium, therefore, should burn in a nuclear fire to carbon.

Why does ordinary helium here on Earth not burst into nuclear flames? In ordinary circumstances it is extremely difficult to get three helium nuclei close together. First, they are surrounded by electrons; second, being positively charged, they repel each other. Only at extremely high temperatures, billions of degrees, would the electrons be torn off and the nuclei have enough energy to overcome electric repulsion and collide with each other. Such are the temperatures required to ignite the helium fire, which, once kindled, would produce enormous amounts of energy and be a million times hotter than ordinary fire. We believe today that in the center of some stars such helium fires are burning and supplying the star with energy for its radiation. The upper left corner star of the constellation Orion is such a one.

There are other kinds of nuclear fire. An important one is the burning of heavy hydrogen. Heavy hydrogen is an isotope of ordinary hydrogen. The nucleus of heavy hydrogen, which is called deuteron, is composed of one proton and one neutron held together by the nuclear forces. Brought in close contact, two deuterons would snap together and form a tightly bound helium nucleus,[3] two protons plus two neutrons. Hence heavy hydrogen burns, and the ashes are helium. This nuclear fire also needs very high temperatures for ignition, but

[3] Detailed studies have shown that the deuterons do not directly form a helium nucleus, as described in the text. They first collide each with another proton, thus forming a helium isotope He^3, and then two of these isotopes unite to an ordinary helium nucleus He^4 and free the two additional protons."

not as high as the helium fire. (The repulsion between deuterons is weaker than between helium nuclei.) In fact heavy hydrogen burning has been achieved by man, but so far only for destructive purposes in the hydrogen bombs.

A most important nuclear fire is the burning of ordinary hydrogen. (See Figure 49.) We believe that this is the kind of fire that burns in the interior of the Sun and keeps the Sun hot by providing the energy supply. It is not obvious how ordinary hydrogen can give rise to a

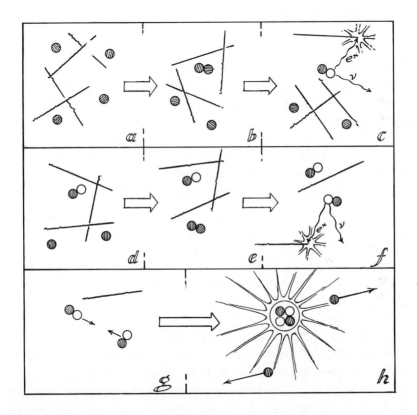

Figure 49. Eight stages of the burning of hydrogen to helium. (a) Four protons (hydrogen nuclei) and four electrons (straight lines symbolizing their fast motion). (b) Two protons close, forming a diproton momentarily. (c) One of the protons changes into a neutron (open circle) with the emission of a positive electron and a neutrino. The positive electron hits a negative electron and annihilates in a light explosion (see section 6 of this chapter). (d) We get a deuteron and two protons. (e) The second pair of protons forms a diproton. (f) The diproton changes over radioactively into a second deuteron as in c. (g) The two deuterons hit. (h) They form a helium nucleus; the energy released is partly radiated (halo), partly transferred to other protons. (In h the electrons are left out.)

nuclear fire, since its nuclei are pure protons and neutrons are needed to form higher nuclei.

Here the mysterious process of radioactivity sets in. In very large amounts of hot hydrogen, it will happen from time to time that two nuclei—two protons, that is—come close together and form temporarily a nucleus consisting of two protons, a diproton. This entity is not very stable, but simple calculations show that once in a while, in a diproton, one of the protons changes radioactively into a neutron, and a deuteron (proton plus neutron) is formed as the end product. The deuterons then burn to helium as previously described.

Thus ordinary hydrogen in large amounts and at high temperature also burns into helium. It is a slow process because deuterons must be made first before the actual burning occurs. The fuel supply for the fire trickles in bit by bit. As a result which we can regard only as benign, the hydrogen fire in the Sun generates and will continue to generate a steady heat supply over many billions of years, without any danger of sudden explosions.

The basic process of nuclear burning, the formation of larger nuclei from smaller ones—carbon from helium, helium from deuterons —is called "fusion." There is also another process with which one can gain energy from nuclei, and this we call fission. The fission process is not very important in our understanding of the universe. Fission rarely happens in nature. Recently, however, man has managed to make use of it, both for energy production in nuclear reactors and for his own destruction in atomic bombs.

The nuclear forces, as we have seen, keep neutrons and protons together in a nucleus. But there is also another disruptive force acting, the electric repulsion between the protons. In all existing nuclei the binding effect of the nuclear forces is greater than the disruptive effect of the electric repulsion. If it were not so, nuclei would not exist. The nuclear forces, however, are very short-ranged; they act only if the particles are very close together, whereas the electric repulsive effects act over large distances. If one could split a nucleus in such a way that the halves were separated by an amount which, though small, would be greater than the range of nuclear forces, the two parts would no longer stick together but would fly apart, driven by the electric repulsion.

Normally it is very hard to "split" a nucleus, but some of the very heavy nuclei, such as a certain uranium isotope or the artificial element plutonium, are on the verge of falling apart. A hit by a single neutron suffices to split such an atom into halves that no longer stick together. The halves fly apart with considerable energy, heating the neighborhood to a high temperature. That is the process of fission. The process is so violent that usually one or two neutrons are chopped off when the nucleus splits. These chopped-off neutrons are of great importance. In a large chunk of fissionable material only one neutron is needed to start a reaction. The one neutron splits the first nucleus, the chopped-off neutrons go on producing further splittings and so on, until a large part of the material has split. This process we call a chain reaction. It can proceed only if the block is so large that the chopped-off neutrons do not leave it before hitting another nucleus. The minimum size required is called the critical size; it is usually a few pounds of material. Any chunk of fissionable material larger than the critical size would develop a chain reaction when hit by one neutron, and thus produce enormous amounts of energy. Atomic reactors are devices in which the amount of fission-

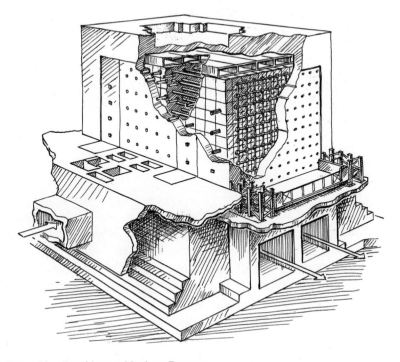

Figure 50. Brookhaven Nuclear Reactor.

able material is kept exactly at critical size; the energy and heat production can be regulated for practical uses. (See Figure 50.)

The two halves of a nucleus produced in fission are themselves smaller nuclei, but their proton-neutron ratio is abnormal. In most cases they have too many neutrons, and therefore they are radioactive. This is why a nuclear reactor is such a prolific producer of radioactive material.

Figure 51. Atomic bomb mushroom.

THE QUANTUM LADDER

Let us now discuss from a more general point of view what we have learned about the structure of matter. It is instructive to consider a special example, and we choose for this purpose a gas of atoms. Most gases consist of molecules, but a few elements, such as neon, sodium, and lithium, do not readily form molecules in gaseous form. You are familiar with these atomic gases in their use as sources of light. The so-called neon tubes that bedizen our city streets are filled with atomic gases, neon or sodium vapor or lithium vapor, each giving a different color when an electric current is discharged through the tube. All these gases are composed of single free atoms.

Let us look at a tube containing sodium vapor. When the electricity is switched off, the temperature of the gas is the same as the temperature outside. At that temperature the rest energy, the energy with which the atoms move around, is about 1/30 electron volt, far below the stability threshold of sodium atoms. So when the atoms hit each other or the walls, they bounce off like hard billiard balls without changing their quantum state. At this temperature the atoms act like elementary particles—they do not show any internal structure. Their electronic pattern remains fixed and unchangeable; all atoms are exactly identical.

Let us raise the temperature of the gas by sending an electric discharge through the tube. When the energy transferred to the atoms by the electric discharge becomes higher than the stability limit, other quantum states are excited. The atoms then emit their own characteristic light when they fall back to their lowest quantum state: sodium atoms radiate yellow light; lithium atoms, red light. The variety of city lights is based upon these typical colors. The excitation of atoms to higher quantum states is the beginning of a breakdown of atomic identity. No longer are all atoms alike; some are in the ground state, some in other states.

We now raise the temperature further, so that the energy of the collisions between the atoms is very much higher than the stability limit—so high, in fact, that the electrons are torn off the atoms. Then the quantum states are all destroyed, and the electrons move like particles without any special wave patterns. We produce the plasma state of the gas, in which electrons and atomic nuclei move around in violently disordered motion. No two motions are exactly equal; the light emitted by the plasma has no characteristic frequency; it is unspecific heat radiation. The atomic nuclei and the electrons, however, still maintain their individuality and identity. They are the elementary particles of the plasma.

Now let us go to a still higher temperature, much too high for the laboratory, where ordinary containers such as glass or metal tubes would disintegrate. It is so high that the particle energies are beyond the stability limit of nuclei. Such temperatures exist only in the centers of stars. Then the nuclei would lose their identity, some would be excited to higher quantum states and emit their characteristic radiation—highly energetic gamma rays. Let us raise the temperature even further, to where the energy becomes so great that the nuclei fall apart into their constituents. Then all nuclear individuality would be lost, the material would form a disordered gas of protons and neutrons mixed with electrons that were torn off the atoms at much lower temperatures. Under these conditions matter would be reduced to a mixture of three elementary particles: protons, neutrons, and electrons, without order.

The sequence we have outlined here we call "quantum ladder." The sequence is established by a gradual increase of energy transfer. At our starting rung of that ladder matter is composed of atoms as individual units whose inner structure is inert and rigid, moving about as billiard balls do. At the next rung the atoms are decomposed into electrons and atomic nuclei, and these particles are now individual units, inert and rigid. At the third rung the nuclei are decomposed into neutrons and protons; the units of matter in that stage are protons, neutrons, and electrons.

The existence of the quantum ladder has made it possible to discover step by step the structure of the natural world. When we investigate phenomena at atomic energies, we need not worry about the internal structure of the nuclei; and when we study the mechanics of gases at normal temperatures, we need not worry about the internal structure of the atoms. In the former case we can consider the nuclei as identical, unchangeable units—that is, as elementary particles; in the latter case each atom may be considered as a unit. Thus the observed phenomena are simpler, and we can understand them without any knowledge of the internal structure of the constituents, which behave as inert units.

We can extend our quantum ladder to lower energies. When we cool down the sodium gas to very low temperatures, the sodium atoms aggregate in a regular array, crystallizing and forming sodium metal. In other materials the step downward from the atom is more interesting. Isolated atoms exist in most materials only at temperatures as high as we find them in flames. At ordinary temperatures most atoms (though not the atoms in sodium, lithium, or neon gas) join in groups and form molecules, which represent the next lower rung in our quantum ladder. They represent individual specific entities whose stability threshold is lower than that of atoms because of the larger size of molecules. It is easier to decompose a molecule into its atoms than to tear the atom apart into its nucleus and electrons.

It is interesting to observe parallel phenomena at different steps of the quantum ladder. We find, for example, energy production when atoms join in molecules—the chemical fire—and energy production when smaller nuclei are fused to larger ones—the nuclear fire. These are two ways of burning, very dissimilar in the amount of energy involved but similar in principle, one occuring at the molecular level, the other at the nuclear level.

At the next step down the quantum ladder are the macromolecules; they are combinations of many ordinary molecules in special arrangements. Under certain conditions macromolecules assemble in the form of large units which exhibit most astonishing properties, of which you will hear more in the next chapter. This is the rung of the quantum ladder where life occurs.

The last and lowest rung is established by matter at very low temperature. Almost all substances crystallize when cooled sufficiently; they form regular arrays of atoms or molecules. Heat motion disappears and total order is established, the order of complete immobility.

When we come to the lowest rungs of the quantum ladder, macromolecules and crystals, the size-stability relation must be applied with some caution. Since macromolecules and crystals are very large objects, one might infer that they would be extremely unstable. But here the unstability inferred from the size-stability relation refers to unimportant properties only. For example, macromolecules have no stiffness, they can be bent and folded with very little exertion of energy; crystals can be brought into internal vibrations with extremely little energy—ordinary sound waves would do it. The important structural properties, however—such as the atomic structure of the macromolecules, or the regular atomic arrangement of the crystal lattice—are quite stable. The electronic patterns of the atoms involved determine these properties, and the stability of the properties therefore is equivalent to the stability of the electronic patterns in atoms.

Each step on the quantum ladder corresponds to matter under certain conditions. (See Figure 52.) The lower the step, the higher the organization and differentiation of matter. Each step downward allows matter to settle in specific forms, which become more varied the farther down we go. At the highest rung we have mentioned so far protons, neutrons, and electrons move without any order. At the next lower step the plasma, protons, and neutrons fall into the ordered pattern of atomic nuclei, but electrons are still in disordered

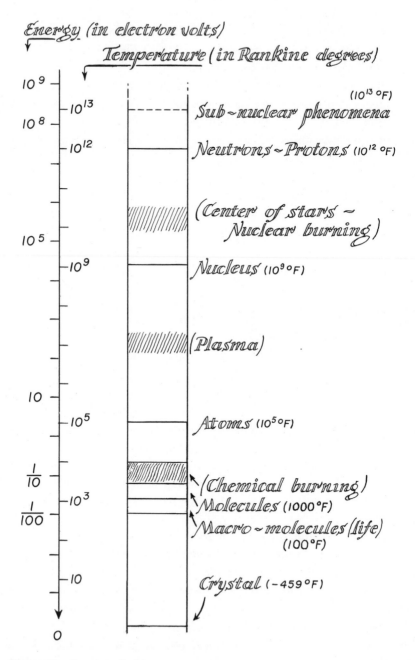

Figure 52. Quantum Ladder.

motion. Farther down the electrons join the nuclei and form atoms; they fall into their typical atomic wave patterns.

At the next lower level atoms join in molecules. The differentiation becomes extensive; there are countless ways of combining atoms to molecules, each corresponding to another well-defined substance. The level of macromolecules contains even more variations—it is the step at which living matter occurs in its various forms and organisms; it is the condition of matter with its widest possibilities. The energy exchanges are low enough for the existence of large complexes of molecules, cells, and organisms, and high enough for the stimulation of growth and development of these entities. At the lowest rung all variety, all differentiation is frozen into unchanging patterns of crystallized substances.

SUBNUCLEAR PHENOMENA

Is there a step in our quantum ladder higher than the state of isolated protons and neutrons? The answer to this question brings us to the frontier of modern elementary particle physics.

Let us recall that energies of many millions of electron volts are needed to decompose the atomic nucleus. Modern high-energy research has not stopped at this limit. In the last decade particle accelerators have been built that attain many hundreds of millions of electron volts. A few machines have passed even the billion mark—in Geneva there is a big accelerator constructed by an effort of fourteen European nations which reaches twenty-eight billion volts. A similar, slightly larger machine is in operation at the Brookhaven National Laboratory, on Long Island.

The principal use of these machines no longer is the study of the structure of the nucleus. It is rather the study of the structure of the protons and neutrons. Here the step is taken to the next higher rung of our quantum ladder. The question is asked whether nucleons have a limit of stability, too, whether there is an energy above which the internal structure of protons and neutrons becomes observable. We investigate the nature of the elementary particles themselves. Because of the small size of these units we expect a very high stability limit, higher than the limit of atomic nuclei. Indeed, not until several hundred million electron volts had been applied were indications of internal structure found.

When such tremendous energies are applied to matter, one observes phenomena that still are not quite understood. These phenomena show that there is structure in the nucleons, but we do not see clearly what that structure is. In this book we shall restrict ourselves to a short description of the phenomena without much detail.

There are four groups of phenomena that occur at these energies. Let us enumerate them:

1. The production of nuclear-field quanta, the mesons
2. The existence of anti-matter
3. The appearance of "strange" particles
4. The short lifetime of the particles

The first phenomenon is reasonably well understood. It will be an everlasting testimony to the creative inventiveness of the human mind that the Japanese physicist Hideki Yukawa in 1935 predicted the existence of these mesons before they actually were discovered. His theoretical reasoning still holds true. The proton and the neutron, he argued, are the source of nuclear forces which keep protons and neutrons together in the nucleus. The nuclear-force field surrounds the proton and the neutron in the same way that the electric field surrounds the electron. An electron radiates light when it is suddenly hit and set in motion. Part of the electric field is torn away, as it were, and spreads out in the form of light rays, or, as we know now, in the form of light quanta. Similarly we expect part of the nuclear field to be torn off when a nucleon is hit with very high energy. We expect to observe a nuclear-field radiation with quanta analogous to the light quanta.

Yukawa predicted the existence of those field quanta, and he even calculated from the properties of the nuclear forces what minimum energy would be needed to produce them. In other words he predicted the stability limit of the protons and the neutrons. Whenever a proton or a neutron is hit by energies higher than a few hundred million volts, these mesons are emitted in all directions—field quanta of nuclear force are created. These quanta are called pi mesons in order to distinguish them from other units which also bear the name meson. The emission of pi mesons is one of the most striking effects at very high energies.

The second group of phenomena is particularly exciting. In 1932 the British theoretical physicist P. A. M. Dirac predicted the existence of an anti-electron, the positron, and his prediction soon afterward was confirmed by Carl D. Anderson when he found the positron in cosmic rays. We already have spoken of this particle in our discussion of radioactivity; the positron is emitted together with a neutrino when a protron transforms into a neutron. The anti-electron is almost identical to the ordinary electron, but it has an opposite charge (positive) and opposite magnetic properties. The most interesting point, however, is this: Whenever an anti-electron (positron) hits an ordinary electron, a form of explosion occurs, and both particles disappear. They annihilate each other, and the energy contained in their masses is transformed into light. Conversely, if enough energy is available, in certain circumstances it can be transformed into an electron-positron pair; thus electrons and positrons can be created from pure energy. The mass of one electron corresponds to the energy of one half million electron volts. The creation of an electron–anti-electron pair, therefore, requires energy greater than 1 Mev.

Atoms contain not only electrons but also nuclei which, in turn, are made up of protons and neutrons. The question arose, are there also anti-protons and anti-neutrons? Because of the higher mass of the protons and neutrons much more energy would be needed to create such an anti-particle-particle pair than to create an electron pair. Several billion Mev would be necessary to produce them. When the 6 Bev machine in Berkeley (Figure 53) was constructed in 1954, the physicists of the whole world anxiously awaited the crucial experiment: Do anti-protons exist?

The answer was yes. The fact that the proton and the neutron also have their anti particles was demonstrated by Segrè, Chamberlain, Wiegand, and Ypsilantis. Thus it has been shown that all the particles of which matter consists do have their anti counterparts. This discovery proves the existence of anti-matter, the existence of atoms made of anti-protons, anti-electrons, and anti-neutrons. Whenever anti-matter gets in touch with ordinary matter, an explosive annihilation sets in. Anti-protons and protons annihilate each other, and the large amount of mass energy is transformed into a burst of nuclear-force quanta, of mesons. This is why anti-matter will never be found on Earth except when it is produced in our machines. It will exist only as long as it is not in contact with ordinary matter.

We come now to the third group of high-energy phenomena, the

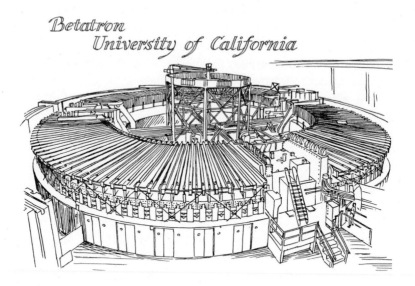

Figure 53. Betatron at Berkeley.

strange particles. When protons or neutrons are bombarded with very high energies, they sometimes transform into a new kind of particle called hyperon. The hyperon is more energetic than the proton and could be considered a higher quantum state of it. An atom also can be lifted to a higher quantum state when the necessary energy difference is supplied. The situation is not quite so simple, however; the production of a hyperon is always accompanied by the production of a so-called K meson, which seems to be also a nuclear-field quantum but of higher energy content than the pi mesons. Physicists are still eagerly groping to understand the significance of this phenomenon.

The fourth group of observations are peculiar to the field of high-energy physics. All the newly discovered units, the pi meson, the K meson, the hyperons, are unstable. They have a very short lifetime, existing only for about a billionth of a second or even less, and then decay into other particles. For example, the nuclear-field quantum, the pi meson, exists for only 10^{-8} second. After this time it transforms itself into an electron-neutrino pair. The situation is complicated by the fact that the electron in this pair turns out to be not an ordinary electron, but a heavy variety with a mass 200 times larger than the ordinary one. It is usually referred to as the mu meson, but this is a poor term, since mesons are field quanta and the heavy electron is an ordinary particle.

The heavy electron itself lives only 10^{-6} second, after which it undergoes another transformation. It transforms itself into a neutrino with the simultaneous creation of an electron-neutrino pair. One pi meson, therefore, ends up as an electron and three neutrinos.

The hyperons undergo similar transformation processes. They change into ordinary protons and neutrons with the creation of an electron-neutrino pair or of a pi meson, which later becomes an electron and three neutrinos.

The nature of these strange transformations is not yet clear. It seems, however, that they are all interrelated. The shortness of the lifetimes is deceptive. For nuclear conditions a billionth of a second is a very long time. After all, a natural time interval in nuclei would be, for example, the time in which a nucleon moves across a nucleus under the influence of nuclear forces. That time interval is much shorter than a billionth of a second—it is of the order of 10^{-22} second. Consequently the instability of the new particles is a weak effect and points toward some specific weak interaction. There is a strong analogy between the decay of the new particles and the radioactive decay of the neutron or proton. In both cases neutrinos are involved. The explanation of these phenomena and their interrelation is a major problem of modern physics.

The highest rung of our quantum ladder offers the greatest challenge to physicists. If we understood these still unexplored phenomena, we might find the answers to still more fundamental problems: Why are there only three kinds of constituents of matter—protons, neutrons, and electrons? Why is there only one elementary unit of charge—the charge of the electron, which is identical but opposite to the charge of the proton? Whenever a new particle is found, its charge is always equal or opposite to this unit.

Finally another question must be raised: When we have explored and understood the phenomena at the highest rung of our quantum ladder, will there be a still higher rung? Only further exploration of nature can ever answer this question. We must continue to seek, and we will find out.

LIFE

Chapter Eight

In the preceding chapters we strove for an insight into the structure of matter. We examined atoms and nuclei and the various combinations of atoms into molecules. Conditions on the Earth are such that most atoms are found in their specific lowest quantum state, and that atoms aggregate and form molecules. The result is that we find on Earth so many materials with well-defined properties, minerals, metals, water, air, etc. But this condition does not hold on the surface of the Sun. There the temperature is so high that molecules cannot exist. They would be torn apart immediately into atoms. Consequently we expect only elements and no molecular compounds on the Sun, and everything in the form of hot vapors. We on Earth enjoy a much more varied environment, since we live in the midst of so many different substances in solid, liquid, and gaseous states.

Materials and chemical substances are inert and passive. They change their forms or chemical constitutions only under the influence of external causes: air is moved by the heating of the Sun, water by wind or by gravity, solids by mechanical or chemical influences such as wind and weather; chemical processes are initiated in the heating and cooling caused by Sun and weather and by the heat flow from the interior of the Earth. A boulder field traversed by a creek may serve as an example (See Figure 54.) The sizes of the rocks in the creek bed vary from small grains to big

Figure 54. Boulder field traversed by creek.

boulders; they were shaped in the events that occurred when debris came tumbling down from some crumbling mountain. Each boulder consists of small crystals, whose structure and hardness are determined by the characteristic properties of silicon oxide, the substance of most of the rocks. The surface of the rocks shows traces of chemical reactions with oxygen in the air or with water from the creek or from rain. But for all the variety, for all the evidence of change, of upheaval or tearing down, of never ending chemical activity, stillness is the quality in such a scene that most impresses us. Nothing is moving except the murmuring water, which once was lifted into the atmosphere by evaporation and now is being drawn into the green valley below by gravity. A gust of wind may shift a few grains of sand or tumble a pebble here or there, but these are mechanical movements that do not seem to affect the inert nature of matter.

There is something else on Earth, however, that does cause motion and change, and it represents a wholly new form in which matter appears. Wherever we look we find manifestations of *life*. The phenomena of life do not seem to fit at all into the framework of the events which we so far have come to expect from matter composed of atoms and molecules. Living matter is not passive and inert. It grows, it multiplies, it moves around on the ground, in the sea, and in the air; its activities seem to be determined by internal and not external causes. Living objects exhibit characteristic forms and shapes contrasting sharply with anything made of ordinary matter. The shapes and sizes recur and repeat and are largely independent of the incidental conditions of their environment. There exists an obvious unit of living matter—the individual organism. It makes definite sense to speak of 1000 bacteria, 1000 rosebushes, or 1000 lions; these units are very much larger than the natural units of matter, the molecules.

Chemical analysis has shown beyond shadow of a doubt that living objects consist of the same kinds of atoms as non-living things. In fact, living matter consists mainly of the four elements carbon, oxygen, hydrogen, and nitrogen, with traces of other elements such as iron, phosphorus, and magnesium. There is not the slightest indication that living matter contains any special material or that the laws of interaction between the atoms are different. The phenomena of life, therefore, must be the result of ordinary interactions between atoms and molecules—very special molecules, to be sure, of a structure and complication that distinguish them strikingly from the molecules of lifeless matter.

Today we are far from a complete understanding of how the interaction of these molecules can give rise to the phenomena of life. In the last two decades, however, biological research has provided so many new insights into the molecular structure of life that we already can form a vague idea of what goes on in living matter. The recent progress of our understanding of life is one of the great scientific achievements, comparable to Newton's and Maxwell's work and to the insights which quantum mechanics has provided. We have a special stake in the understanding of these structures, since not only are our own bodies living matter, but life in some form composes the most important part of our environment.

THE MOLECULES OF LIFE

Life exists in many shapes. Let us first look at a simple form of life, a bacterium.[1] (See Plate VI.) It is ten-thousandth of an inch long, shaped like a sausage, with a skin and a jellylike substance inside. Such a unit is called a "cell." In order to understand the essential features of this living object, let us compare it with a similarly shaped non-living object, say a plastic sausage-shaped skin filled with a jellylike substance such as fat or gelatine. The walls and the inside of the latter would be homogeneous; the inside and the con-

---

[1] We are describing here the bacterium *Escherichia coli*. (See Plate VI.) There are many different kinds of bacteria, and not all have the same properties.

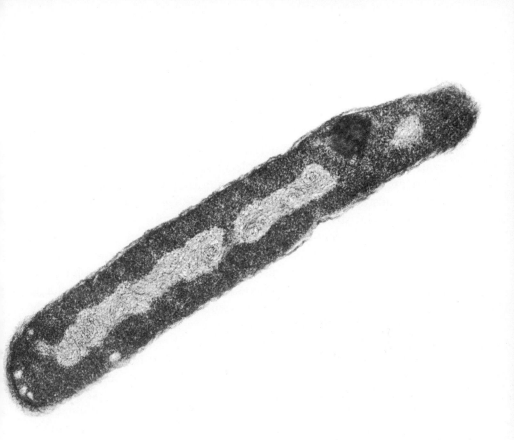

Plate VI. An electron microscope picture of a bacterium (E. Coli). Magnification 48,000x.

tainer would consist of a large number of identical molecules of the same kind. The molecules of the plastic make up the skin; the fat or gelatine molecules make up the content. In a cell, however, the situation is vastly more complicated and vastly more differentiated. The units of which the material consists are complicated combinations of large numbers of molecules, so called macromolecules. There are not just one or two kinds, but as many as five thousand different kinds of macromolecules in a single cell, each having a well-defined special structure.

But this complication is not the main difference. Let us put the two things, the plastic bag filled with fat or gelatine and the actual bacterium, in a so-called nutrient solution—that is, a solution of sugar, phosphate, and ammonia. The plastic bag won't change much. Some of its content might seep out through the pores of the skin and some of the solution might seep in. But the bacterial cell would change a lot—it would grow; more macromolecules would be formed inside the cell. The molecules of the solution seep through the skin into the cell, where they are decomposed, and the atoms rearrange to form new macromolecules. When this process has gone on for a time, an even stranger event occurs. The cell divides into two, and each part starts growing for itself. At the end, when all the nutrient material is used up, the relatively simple molecules of the nutrient—sugar, phosphate, ammonia—are all transformed into the complicated macromolecules of the cells. This is the process of life.

Essentially there are two types of macromolecules in the cell, the *proteins* and the *nucleic acids*. The bulk of the cell is made up of proteins; nucleic acids are in the minority, but they play a very decisive rôle.

Let us start with a description of the proteins. They are large units built up of amino acid molecules, the type which we described in the last chapter. The amino acid molecules are arranged like beads on a string, one following the other in a linear array, often as many as 1000 in a row. Here we meet a typical property of the macromolecules of life: they are chains of smaller units, put in a certain well-defined order—long chains, in which one molecule follows the other.

The order in which these units are arrayed is of great importance. We find twenty different kinds of amino acids in proteins. They bear such names as glycine or alanine, but we shall call them simply by the letters of the alphabet, a, b, c—and we need twenty letters for this. A protein, then, is described when we enumerate its amino acids in the order in which they are arranged. (See Figure 55.)

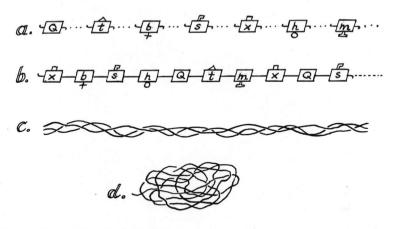

Figure 55. Protein Structure.
a. Different amino acids, simplified. The two hooks symbolize the carboxyl group on one side, the amino group on the other. They hook up and bind the amino acids together. b. An amino acid chain. In rows c and d this chain is represented as a line. c. A fibrous protein. The chains wind like the strands in a rope. d. A globular protein. The chains are coiled up in a skein.

Any array of letters like c, f, m, u, a, d, etc. would identify a particular protein. Then thousands of letters would be needed in order to describe the big ones among them. There are uncounted ways of arranging twenty different kinds of amino acids in a row of 1000. Each arrangement is another protein. We can get a feeling for the immensity of the number of the possible proteins by observing that 1000 letters take up approximately two thirds of a page of a book. Each way of filling these pages with letters, whether the sequence contains actual words or not, corresponds to another kind of protein.

The proteins found in living matter are only a small part of all possible proteins. They comprise only the "sensible" combinations of amino acids, the combinations that are used in the structure and chemistry of the cell. They correspond, as it were, to the book pages containing meaningful sentences. Still the number of such sensible proteins is immense. For example, the proteins that make up the human skin are slightly different in every human being. This is why it is impossible to graft human skin of one person upon another except when the two are identical twins.

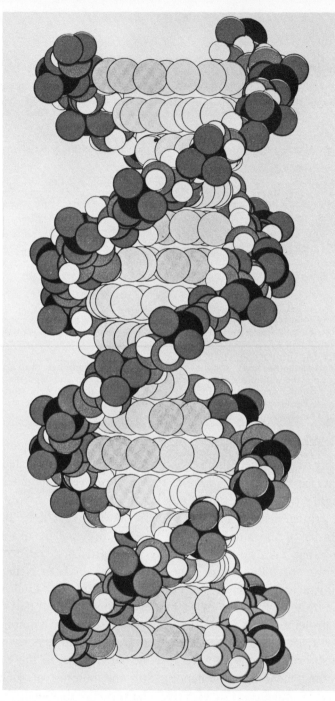

Plate VII. This model of a portion of the DNA molecule shows clearly the variety of atoms present and the complex spiral structure.

The bacterial cell is one of the simplest living units and therefore contains a much smaller variety of proteins. There are "only" about 5000 different kinds of proteins in the cell. They differ from each other in many ways. Some are stiff and look like fibers; they serve as material for the skin of the cell, for internal divisions and membranes (not unlike the proteins in the human skin). Other proteins are pliable, so much so that the long chain of amino acids is all coiled up in a skein. Called globular proteins, they are able to move around, and they make up most of the jellylike content of the cell.

These latter proteins are chemical agents; they can engage in chemical reactions, which are needed in the process of growth, as we shall see later in more detail. One needs quite complicated mechanisms for such specialized tasks; that is why some proteins are very intricate combinations of molecules.

Next we come to the second type of macromolecules, the nucleic acids. They represent only a small part of the cell however, as we shall see, the decisive part. The most important nucleic acid is deoxyribonucleic acid—DNA for short. (See Plate VII.) DNA is again a chain of units arranged in a linear array, one after the other. The units are not amino acids, but molecules called nucleotides. There are only four different kinds: cytosine, guanine, thymine, adenine. We are not interested here in the details of their structure; they contain atoms of carbon nitrogen, hydrogen, oxygen, and phosphorous. Let us call them simply C, G, T, and A. The units of the chain forming our macromolecule DNA are actually a little more complicated. They are pairs of nucleotides. The following pairs are used as beads in this chain: C with G and A with T.

Because of the arrangement of the pairs of nucleotides, it is perhaps better to describe the nucleic acids as a ladder rather than as a chain. (See Figure 56.) Each rung of the ladder is one of the pairs. It makes a difference which of the nucleotides in the pair is on the right side and which on the left side of the rung. Hence there are four different kinds of rungs: CG, GC, TA, and AT; they follow each other step after step in a well-defined order which characterizes the DNA-molecule ladder. In addition this ladder is twisted in a spiral, so that the whole macromolecule looks more like a spiral staircase, each step being one of the nucleotide pairs. In living cells these molecules have enormous lengths—they contain as many as ten to one hundred million pairs of nucleotides in a row. When found in

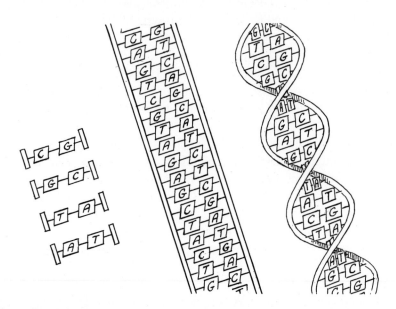

Figure 56. Schematic picture of the DNA molecule. (a) The four units of the chain. (b) The ladder without twist. (c) The actual form of the twisted ladder.

the cell, the spiral is all coiled up in a tight skein. With the skein unfolded, the total length of the spiral ladder would be about a half inch in bacteria cells, and as long as several feet in human cells. (See Plate VIII.)

Here we must pause and think. What we have facing us is a molecular structure of the size of inches or feet—a macroscopic size, as large as objects on our table. But still it is one single molecule. It is, of course, the large number of nucleotides that causes these enormous sizes; each pair of nucleotides is very small, as small as we expect ordinary non-living molecules to be, say some 10^{-7} cm. But 10 or 100 million in a row amount to lengths in meters.

There is some reason that the maintenance of life should need such long molecules. We shall see this soon in greater detail. At present let us be content to emphasize the tremendous variety of possible DNA arrangements. We already have observed the enormous number of ways one can build up a protein chain of 1000 amino acid beads when there are twenty varieties of beads.

In the case of DNA we have only four types of beads, but 10 to 100 millions of them! It is important to realize that the restriction of

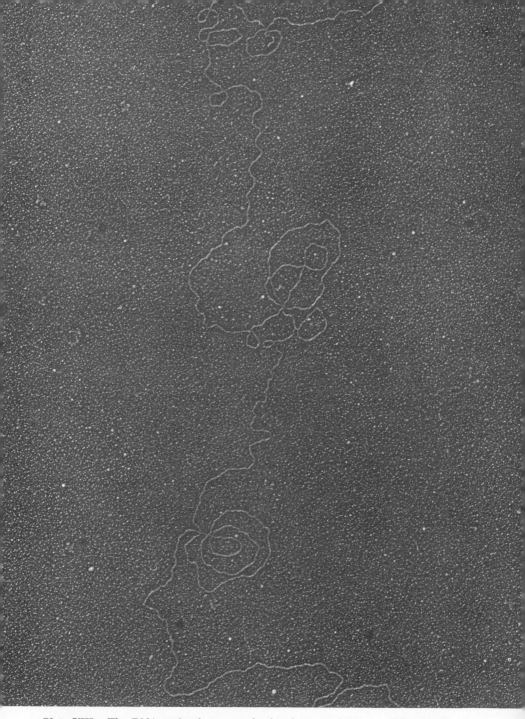

Plate VIII. The DNA molecule as seen in the electron microscope. Microscopic plus photographic enlargement about 20,000x. The DNA molecule of a bacterium in this magnification would be about 200 yards long.

bead types to four (instead of the twenty in the proteins) reduces the number of different arrangements, but it reduces it by not very much. This reduction is vastly overcompensated by the very much larger number of beads. Instead of having the twenty letters, we now have only the four. But it is possible to have a written language with even two letters; this is done in the Morse code, where only dots and dashes are used. True enough, one needs on the average three or four Morse signals per letter, so that 1000 signals would correspond to only a fifth of a page. But a DNA molecule (apart from having four and not two types of symbols) contains 10^7 to 10^8 rungs, many thousand times more than a protein, which would correspond to a book of 1000 to 10,000 pages. Thus the number of different ways to build a DNA molecule is as large as the number of possible arrangements of letters (sensible and not sensible) in a book of 10,000 pages or more!

We soon shall see that this variety is connected with the variety of life, that the arrangement of the four types of pairs in the DNA molecule is the book which tells the cell what to do and how to develop. Only one question remains, how to read this book.

THE CHEMICAL PROCESS OF LIFE

Let us now come back to what we called the process of life—the growth of the bacteria cell and its division into two new ones when it is immersed in the nutrient solution of sugar, phosphate, and ammonia. It is a most interesting and puzzling process.

Sugar and ammonia are very simple molecules. Therefore there must be in the cell of the bacterium a mechanism able to do two things: first, to build the twenty kinds of amino acid molecules and the four nucleotides from sugar and ammonia, and second, (this second step is much the harder) to combine the amino acids in the correct order to form the thousand different proteins and to provide replica of the nucleic acids in the process of division.

The first task, the fabrication of the "beads," is done, as we have mentioned before, by certain proteins in the cell. These proteins have the ability to decompose nutrient molecules after they have seeped in through the skin, and to rearrange their atoms into amino acids or nucleotides.

The second task, the arrangement of the beads in the correct order to form the new proteins or the new nucleic acids, is the one in which the large nucleic-acid chains are involved.

The details of this mechanism are not well known. It is a very complicated process, and that is why it needs so many and such complicated proteins and nucleic acids. Only in the last two decades have the basic principles of this mechanism been discovered. We shall try to present them in a simplified form.

There is one necessity for this process—energy. When amino acids are formed and when they are hitched to one another into proteins, energy is necessary to move the parts at the right place and to put them together with the correct bonds.

Let us have a look at the energy production. The sugar molecules of the nutrient solution in which the bacterium was immersed contain energy. We know that the burning of sugar can release much energy in the form of heat when the sugar is transformed into carbon dioxide and water. The heat energy would be quite useless, however, for the purpose here, since it is irregular random motion which cannot be used for purposeful molecule construction. We mentioned in the last chapter that it is possible by special "rigging" to turn the energy of burning from heat into energetic quantum states of certain molecules. Here in the cell certain specific proteins do this rigging. These proteins are able to attract a sugar molecule to their surface. There the molecule is forced to fall apart into groups of atoms, which are rearranged by the protein to form carbon dioxide and water. This process is equivalent to "burning." What happens with the energy released in this process? The protein also attracts molecules of another kind, which are kept close to the decaying sugar. These molecules (always present in the cell) are called adenosine triphosphates, ATP for short. They can assume two quantum states, one of lower and one of higher energy, and therefore they can act as storage for the energy extracted from the sugar. Whenever sugar is burned by the protein, ATP molecules are lifted into their higher quantum states. If energy is needed somewhere else in the cell for a molecule synthesis, the ATP molecule will get there and deliver the energy by falling back into its less energetic quantum state.[2] The ATP energy carriers have another advantage—they carry very

[2] In fact the state of lower energy is the molecule adenosine diphosphate (ADP). The loading with energy is accompanied by acquisition of another phosphor atom; the state of higher energy then is adenosine triphosphate (ATP).

small amounts of energy. The energy liberated by the burning of one sugar molecule is divided up among about forty ATP molecules. The energy is changed into small coins, so to speak, and can be distributed more easily to the many activities for which it is needed.

Now we come to the next question: How are the molecules and macromolecules put together in the cell? Let us start with the beads making up the protein chains, such as the more than twenty-four types of amino acids. The atoms contained in the amino acids can all be found in the nutrient solution; they are contained in the sugar and ammonia molecules and in other salts. These molecules enter the cell through the pores of the skin. So all that is necessary is to decompose these simple molecules of the nutrient solution and to put the parts together to form an amino acid. It is again the proteins that perform the essential step. A group of specific proteins is assigned to the production of each type of amino acid. These proteins have the property of attracting the right molecules of the nutrient and, with the help of the energy supplied by ATPs, of reshuffling the atoms until they produce the special amino acid. What happens is this: When the protein encounters sugar and ammonia, the atoms of the latter two become attached to the protein at certain special corners. These corners are so arranged that the atoms, once attached, are forced to fall into the scheme of the amino acid to be formed.

There are also other proteins which, in the same way, produce nucleotides from the molecules of the nutrient.

All these processes are examples of the astonishing properties of proteins. They can perform and direct chemical reactions such as the energy transfer from burning sugar to ATP and the formation of amino acids and nucleotides. Proteins with this ability usually are called enzymes. They are much more complicated than the simpler proteins which are not enzymes and which serve only to give the cell structure and to regulate the flow of materials. The proteins can build up all the constituents of which they are made. But they cannot put them together. The proteins produce the letters, but do not put them together in words. The letters are there, but where is the author to compose the words and sentences?

THE MASTER PLAN OF LIFE

The most important question must still be answered: How are the amino acids put together to form proteins? This step contains all the secrets of the life of a bacterium, since, as we have seen, it is the different types of proteins that perform all the important steps in the chemical life of the cell. Where in the cell is the master plan hidden for each of the many thousand proteins, the plan that determines the order in which the amino acids follow each other along the string? Let us recall that each one of the proteins is a string of roughly a thousand amino acids (sometimes more, sometimes less) and that if we ascribe to each type of amino acid one letter of the alphabet, the array of the amino acids corresponds to an array of a thousand letters, as many as we find on about a page of this book. To specify the order of amino acids in 5000 proteins we would need several thousand pages of a book like this one. Where is the information to be found in the cell? We only need to remember that the nucleic acid macromolecules have in them the possibility of expressing the content of many thousand pages of a book. The order in which the four types of nucleotide pairs are arranged along the winding spiral could give us that information. There are just enough possibilities in the order of the steps of the inch-long nucleic acid in the bacterium to determine the 5000 proteins that make up the bacterium.

The big question poses itself: How does the order of nucleotides in the nucleic acid determine the order of amino acids in the proteins? How is the information contained in the steps of the spiral transmitted to the newly formed proteins? How can the cell "read" this book of many thousands of pages and follow the instructions when it grows and divides?

We don't know much about this. We know only that such transmission of information does occur. In a very simplified way we can picture the protein formation as follows: A group of steps of the spiral ladder attracts one kind of amino acid, the next group of steps attracts another kind, and so forth. The steps are so arranged that, in this way, the amino acids align themselves in the right order in which they are supposed to form a protein. Proteins are formed all along the nucleic acid ladder, which is long enough to accommodate all 5000 proteins needed for the bacterium. This description of protein formation is vastly simplified. We know that the actual processes are far more complicated, and the details are still largely unknown. Nevertheless, our picture should help to clarify what we now believe are the fundamental processes in a bacteria cell.[3]

Let us summarize: The cell is made of different kinds of proteins; the simple ones make up the skin and the structural framework. Others burn sugar and produce the energy-bearing ATP molecules; the most complicated proteins produce amino acids from the chemicals provided by the nutrient. The cell also contains a few large nucleic acid molecules which are able to combine the amino acids in the correct order, so that they form new proteins of all kinds needed in the process of growing.

When the cell reaches a certain size, some largely unknown factors cause a rearrangement of the proteins, and the cell divides into two equal smaller cells. At that stage it is necessary to duplicate the all-important nucleic acids, since each cell needs a set of them for further growth. The duplication of such a long and well-ordered molecule is not an easy process. We don't know exactly how nature does it, but we can imagine a way in which it could perhaps occur. Here is a simple mechanism which would duplicate the spiral ladder making up the long DNA molecule.

Each rung of the ladder, you will remember, is a definite pair of nucleotides. At cell-division time the ladder is cut in two parts lengthwise, by breaking each rung in the middle (See Figure 57). The two partners of the pairs constituting the rungs simply separate, and two half ladders are formed. Now we must remember that the cell at that point contains free-swimming nucleotides, which were produced by special proteins (enzymes). Then each half rung finds

---

[3] Actually the proteins are not put together directly by the DNA molecule. First, copies are made of those parts of the DNA which contain the information regarding one specfic protein. These copies are in the form of another nucleic acid, RNA (ribonucleic acid), which consists of a chain of single nucleotides, not pairs, as in DNA. Each of these copies is, of course, much shorter than the original DNA, since it contains only the part concerning one protein. We call them "messenger RNA." There is a different one for each protein to be formed. They move away from the cell "nucleus," which is the part of the cell where the DNA is found, and get to the so-called ribosomes, special spots in the cell devoted to protein production. There the messenger RNA finds the different amino acids, which then are put into the right order to form a specific protein. A group of beads in the RNA chain attracts one kind of amino acid, the next group of beads attracts another kind, and so forth. The other chemicals in the ribosomes are needed to help the amino acids to find their right place along the messenger RNA and to help them to become attached to each other.

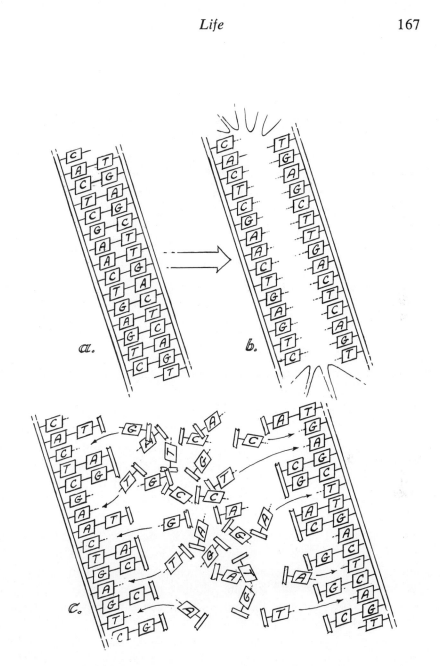

Figure 57. Multiplication of DNA. (a) DNA molecule; for clarity the spiral winding is removed. (b) The lengthwise split of DNA. (c) Each half of a DNA collects the correct nucleotides and forms a new complete DNA molecule, identical with the original one.

the corresponding nucleotide in the cell and forms again a full rung. At the end of this process two complete ladders with exactly the same order of steps are established; after division each goes into one of the newly formed cells.

We now have a vague idea how a bacterium grows and multiplies. When a few bacteria are put into a nutrient solution, the process of life transforms the simple but energy-rich nutrient molecules into complicated molecules of more and more bacteria until the nutrient is used up. This process is possible only because of the existence of the DNA macromolecules, which not only determine the structure of the build-up but also reproduce themselves for each cell division, so that the build-up can go on with ever increasing multiplicity.

VIRUS AND MAN

So far we have described the structure and the life process of a bacterium. What about the other forms of life from virus to man, including all plants and animals? It is remarkable that some of the essential features are the same in all manifestations of life, in spite of the great variety of forms and species.

Let us look at the two extremes in this scale, at the virus (See Plate IX) and at man. A virus is much smaller than a bacterium. It consists of a nucleic acid contained in a coat made of simple proteins. It has none of the complicated proteins that produce amino acids or ATP or nucleotides. It does not need them. A virus leads the life of a parasite. It can live and multiply only when it attacks some other cell. Clinging to the skin of the host cell, it sheds its nucleic acid into the cell, and there it uses the amino acids and nucleotides of the host (and the ATP energy sources of the host) for its own duplication and for the acquisition of a new coat. In fact it works so fast that soon the cell is full of newly made viruses, which burst the skin and kill the cell. (See Plate X.) Thus viruses produce diseases. They attack certain kinds of cells in our bodies and kill them by using up cell material for their own reproduction. Naturally the nucleic acid of the virus needs to "know" much less than the one of a bacterium. It only needs to produce the proteins for its coat and to reproduce itself. No other protein is needed, because the host cell supplies everything else. It is no surprise that the nu-

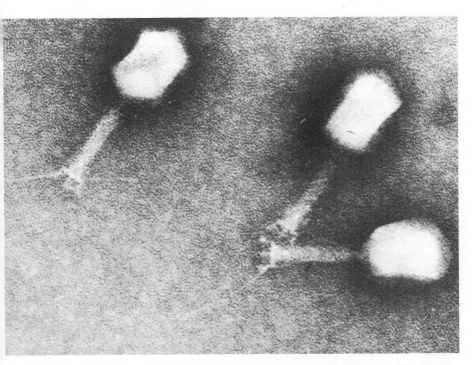

Plate IX. Three virus units as shown by an electron microscope. Magnification 18,000x.

cleic acid of a virus is very much shorter than the one found in a bacterium. Its spiral ladder contains only about 100,000 steps. This short length fits very well into our picture of the nucleic acid as the carrier of information. A virus is the simplest living unit; it has the shortest DNA chain.

Let us now go over to the most complicated living thing, man, and compare him with the bacterium. First of all, the bacterium is one single cell; man is an agglomeration of very many cells of different kinds. But in spite of their variety, human cells are similar to the bacterium cell in many essential features. They also are made of proteins—simple fiber-shaped ones for the skin and the structure, complicated globular ones for the performance of chemical reactions. They contain ATP molecules, which carry energy around. Last but not least, each cell contains DNA molecules. The DNA molecules are, as expected, very long, about a hundred times longer than the bacteria DNAs. The spiral ladders in human cells are as long as six feet when stretched out in a straight line. In its actual form, however, the ladders are coiled and take up very little space in each cell. They contain several billions of steps! The enormity of this array, of course, has something to do with the fact that a human being is a more complicated organization than a bacterium.

Although all human cells contain the same DNA, they are very different in every other respect. Each type of cell serves a different purpose. The skin cells protect the body, the stomach cells produce the chemicals needed for digestion, the muscle cells are able to contract and perform physical work, the cells of the retina in the eye are light-sensitive, and then there are the nerve cells.

The nervous system is perhaps the most important innovation in the progression from the bacterium to higher species. Nerves are long strands of special cells which, like telephone wires, transmit messages from one place to another, though at lower velocity and by a different mechanism. When light falls upon the retina, the stimulus is transmitted to the brain; when the skin is stimulated at some place, the message is transported to other places. Vice versa, a stimulus originating in the brain goes via the nerves to any muscle of the body and produces contraction. The brain itself is a complicated tangle of an enormous number of nerve cells, as many as ten billion, which are interconnected and arranged in a way which we do not understand yet. But this tremendous unit of nerve cells is able to react to the stimuli coming from the outside. It can think and feel.

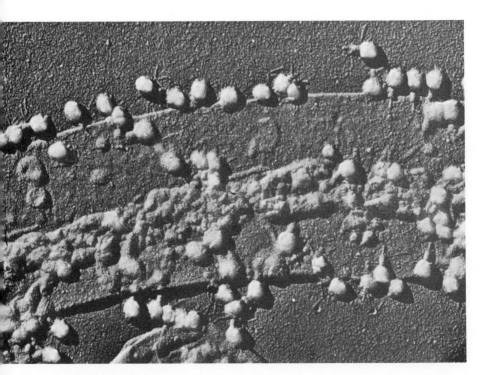

Plate X. A bacterium cell sheds many virus units which were produced inside. Electron microscope magnification 48,000x.

There is an essential biological difference between the bacterium and man. When the bacterium grows and divides, it produces everything that is needed in one single cell. When a human being grows, very different cells must be fabricated—skin cells, muscle cells, bone, nerves, etc. Each part of the body must follow a different master plan.

This fact raises a most formidable problem which is not yet solved. According to our present knowledge, every cell contains a DNA molecule which possesses the whole information of the body; it could produce all the proteins ever used in man. Evidently none of the cells produces them all. How then does the cell know which part of the DNA master plan concerns its growth? How does it eliminate all other parts and make use only of the appropriate one?

Consider the problem of growth and development of the individual. We know that at the very beginning the embryo consists of one cell, which divides into a few more, each of them alike. But soon specialization occurs. Some of the cells develop into the spine, others into the limbs, others into the gastric canal, and others into the nervous system. Although they all have the same nucleic acid, they develop differently. How is this done?

We notice this peculiar selective ability of cells when we observe the healing of a wound. Somehow the cells adjacent to the wound "know" how to grow and to multiply in such manner and direction that the original structure is re-established. Only those proteins are produced that fit the pattern and cause the desired structure to develop.

Very probably the explanation of this problem goes along the following lines: The nucleic acid molecule is so arranged that the effectiveness of its different parts depends upon the environment. At the beginning of the development of the embryo only those parts of the DNA are effective that produce the early cells. Then the presence of the newly created proteins has an influence upon the DNA such that other parts become effective, thus creating a new set of proteins. So we see that at each step of the development a different part of the DNA becomes active. In each cell of the human body only that part of the DNA corresponding to the specific needs of the particular cell is at work. The other parts are held inactive by some peculiar chemical effects of the environment, effects that are today very little understood. Experiments with various embryo cells have shown, for example, that a cell from a position where it was destined to become part of an animal's tail will develop as part of the animal's head if it is transplanted into the environment where the head is supposed to grow.

The order of nucleotides in the DNA is not maintained exactly when a new individual is formed. The chain of molecules is so tremendous that small deviations here and there do not fundamentally alter the development of the individual; they cause only small modifications. Thus no individual is exactly like another. As a consequence of sexual reproduction, these modifications are mixed in every new generation. Children are basically like the parents, but different in details. Their DNA is a copy of about half of the DNA of the father and half of the mother. Here is a fundamental difference between living individuals and atoms. Two atoms of the same kind are identical in every respect—they are completely alike. Two living beings of the same species never are completely identical. The immensely long chain of the DNA provides many possibilities for variation within a given species, and it is the variations that make life so interesting and exciting.

THE SOURCES OF NUTRITION

The material that forms human beings and makes them grow—where does it come from? The virus solves this problem very simply. It is a parasite, and it forms its progeny inside the host cell, using up the amino acids and nucleotides produced by the host. The bacterium is more independent; it builds up the amino acids and nucleotides by means of special proteins, but it needs to be immersed in a nutrient solution of sugar and other chemicals. Man must eat in order to live and grow. He eats living material, such as plants or meat. In this respect man and the other animals are less independent than a bacterium. We could not live off a sugar-and-ammonia solution because human cells cannot synthesize the essential amino acids. We are parasites in this respect. We must get our supply of amino acids and nucleotides from other living material. The proteins in our food are broken up, in the process of digestion, into the amino acids of which they were made. The human cells then use these amino acids in order to build up the proteins needed for their own growth and for chemical work.

As far as our energy needs are concerned, for the work of our muscles and for the synthesis of proteins, we are doing the same as the bacterium. We, too, have proteins in our cells which can make use of the energy liberated by the "burning" of sugar and store it in small portions in the quantum states of the ATP molecule. These molecules are the energy carriers of the body; they are taken up by a muscle when it contracts and does work, or by a cell using energy to produce new proteins.

The bacteria need sugar; we need amino acids and sugar. Where does all this material come from? We and all other living beings, including the bacteria, use up sugar by burning it to CO_2 and water. We also use up amino acids since, after death, our bodies disintegrate —that is, the amino acids decay into carbon and the other simple chemicals of which they are made. Both the sugar molecules and the amino acids (and nucleotides) are energy-rich combinations of atoms. And the supply of these energy-rich molecules? There must be a place where sugar is synthesized in order to make life possible and where amino acids are made for animals. If there were no such place, living beings would soon have used up all the available supply.

Plants are the places where this synthesis occurs. The green color of plants comes from a chemical called chlorophyll, which is, next to the DNA, the most crucial molecule for the existence of life on Earth. It is not nearly as large a molecule as DNA, but it has an intricate structure with which it performs a most important function. When exposed to the rays of the Sun, chlorophyll makes use of the energy of sunlight and rebuilds energy-rich molecules, such as sugar, from their "ashes," carbon dioxide and water. Sun energy is transformed into chemical energy.

The chlorophyll molecules work in the cells of green plants. A plant gets the water from the soil, the carbon dioxide from the air, and the energy from the rays of the sun when they fall upon the green leaves or blades.

Sugar contains less oxygen than CO_2 and water. Hence, as a by-product, free oxygen develops when this process goes on. All the oxygen in the atmosphere was produced by plants when their chlorophyll did its sugar-producing job. We could not breath were it not for the plants' constant work, producing oxygen.

Chlorophyll molecules are fabricated whenever a green plant grows. The plant cells are similar to the cells we already have described; they are, however, even more independent than the bacterium. Not only do they have proteins, which make all the necessary amino acids, but also they can fabricate chlorophyll, which then, with the help of sunlight, synthesizes sugar. In this way plants live and grow without a nutrient sugar solution and without "eating" living matter. All they need are light, carbon dioxide, water, and a few chemicals such as ammonia, which is found in the soil. In this respect they are ideal living systems. In fact the plants are the only kind of living matter that is "productive"; they make all their material with the help of light from simple minerals. All other forms of life are "destructive." They need the energy-rich material formed by plants, and use it to produce their own structures. Animals and man are the worst offenders. They need not only energy-rich material like sugar, but also highly organized material such as amino acids in order to build up their own cells. On the other hand we and the animals can boast of a much higher organization, vastly higher than in other forms of life. In particular we must be proud of our nervous system, which gives us co-ordinated sense perception and motion, and last but not least, makes thinking possible.

What is life? From our point of view it is a manifestation of some special molecule structures which reproduce themselves continuously and induce other molecular structures to form according to an established scheme, different in each species but similar in principle. Only under very special conditions can atoms aggregate to form living matter. The temperature must be low enough so that heat motion does not destroy the complicated fabric of macromolecules. It must not be too cold either, since life is possible only if proteins and nucleic acids can perform their chemical synthesis; for this activity some heat motion is necessary. If the cell material freezes, all chemical work comes to a standstill. Sunlight must be available for the synthesis of energy-rich molecules, but not too much—the temperatures must remain moderate. Here on Earth obviously these conditions are fulfilled; the surface of our planet abounds with green plants and various strange combinations of atoms which we call living organisms.

Although many questions of human and animal development are unanswered, the following ideas stand out clearly: Each species with all its organs, nerves, bones, and brain develops biologically from its germ cell according to the plan laid out in the nucleic acid macromolecule. Here atomic physics and life in its highest form are intimately connected. Each nucleotide in the long chain has its well-defined quantum state, which is the basis of its specific character. They are tied together by electrons in typical quantum patterns, which are stable enough to maintain the order of the chain in spite of the heat motions and other disturbing effects in the cell. Upon this order rest not only the development of the individual but also the propagation of the species. The stability of the quantum patterns in the DNA is the guarantee that the children are basically like their parents, that the species is maintained. The various forms of life are a reflection of the various ways of combining nucleotides in the nucleic acid. The constancy of these forms, the recurrence in each generation, is a reflection of atomic stability.

EVOLUTION

Chapter Nine

WHAT HAPPENED AT THE BEGINNING?

When man contemplates nature, as we have done in this book, the question of how things were created is bound to arise. We yearn for some coherent story that will tell us how this world came to be. This is why all religions and many philosophical systems give accounts of the beginning of the world and why some of them also prophesy the ultimate end.

Is there any scientific answer to these questions? As always in science, answers can be only partial. Our scientific knowledge of nature is constantly growing. Every new scientific discovery adds something to it. Still there are many phenomena which we do not understand. Therefore when we try to reconstruct the course of nature for time periods that are very distant from now, past or future, or very far away in space, our conclusions necessarily will be vague. In particular, when we speculate about matter under conditions very different from on Earth, we are bound to make many mistakes. The shortcomings of our understanding then are magnified vastly. Since we are forced to extrapolate our experience, a small error or misinterpretation can lead us to completely wrong conclusions. Still it is tempting, and many scientists have been tempted, to give a possible or probable account of the past as the basis of our present knowledge, a story that tells how the world could perhaps have evolved and taken the shape it has.

Science is knowledge of nature, but this knowledge also implies an awareness of the limits of our present understanding. We therefore must not expect a complete account. For example, we do not know anything about the real beginning of nature—if there ever was such a beginning. All we can do is to go back as far as our present knowledge allows us to go; that is as far as we can reasonably trust our conclusions. Our story will not answer every question regarding the beginning of the universe. It will have to start at some later day, at a time when our world was in a state about which we have some information. The earliest state of matter known to us is the one in which it appears in the form of dilute hydrogen gas. Our story will tell us a restricted tale, but an impressive one nevertheless, the development of matter from a hydrogen-gas nebula to the living world.

Among the many questions that cannot be answered today there is the one raised by the expansion of the universe. In the first chapter we learned that all galaxies are moving away from us. If this movement has gone on unchanged in the past, there must have been a moment when all matter in the universe was concentrated at one spot—the "beginning" of the expansion. We do not know whether the expansion goes on forever unchanged. If no change has occurred in the past, we must conclude that ten to twenty billion years ago the galaxies were all crowded into a very small area; matter would have been under most abnormal conditions of concentration. Very little can be said about this hypothetical beginning of the universe, except that conditions would have been completely different from anything known to us.

There is a school of scientists who defend an interesting point of view that avoids this abnormal state of the universe at the beginning. According to the speculations of this school, the expansion of the universe is accompanied by a continuous creation of matter in space. Whenever the expansion leaves an abnormally large space between galaxies, new matter is supposedly created in these spaces, and this new matter assembles into new stars and galaxies. The production of new matter, according to this theory, would be just ample enough to keep the space between galaxies roughly the same in spite of the expansion. This interesting idea shows that it is possible to conceive, at least, of an expanding universe without a beginning and without an end. There was no "crowding" of galaxies many billion years ago because there were fewer galaxies at that time; most of the galaxies we see have been created in the time interval between the apparent beginning and today. Conversely, there will be no thinning out of galaxies tomorrow because new ones are created constantly. Galaxies are born incessantly and move away from one another into infinite space. This is what the expansion of the universe means according to that school of scientists.

There is little fact to support these ideas, but there is nothing to contradict them either. It is true that the notion of matter's being created out of nothing in space contradicts our ordinary ideas of conservation of matter and energy. However, the amount required to keep the universe from thinning out is so small that one never would observe it in a laboratory. All that is needed is one hydrogen atom per year created in each cubic mile of the universe; it would be impossible to observe these infinitesimals directly.

Today these conjectures are pure speculation and have no base in any actual observation. It is possible, however, that future observations and a better understanding of what is going on in and between galaxies might someday lead to more substantial ideas about the ultimate beginning and end of this world, ideas based on facts and not on fancies. There is no question, however, that the speculations about continuous creation of matter are of some interest, because they show that an expanding universe without beginning or end is at least logically possible.

THE EVOLUTION OF STARS

So we cannot today give an account of the creation and development of the universe as a whole. We know very little about the way the galaxies were created or how they develop. We set ourselves a narrower goal. We have almost enough knowledge and insight for a description of a partial development—the formation of matter as we know it on Earth from a dilute hydrogen gas. Our galaxy and other galaxies are full of so-called interstellar gas, which spreads over vast spaces and consists mostly of hydrogen. There is so much of this gas that it makes up a good part of the total mass of the galaxy. We do not know much about the origin of this hydrogen gas. Part of it no doubt was expelled during star explosions, but to a great extent it must have been there before any stars were formed. Here is the beginning of our story, in which we intend to show how all things we see and live with have evolved from such hydrogen gases.

A word of warning is in place, however. Even this partial story of the universe is based upon rather unsafe conclusions and theories concerning the behavior of matter under very abnormal conditions. Hence many of the statements in this chapter are hypothetical and much less safe and less solidly founded than the content of the previous chapters.

The Hydrogen Gas. We start with an enormous cloud of hydrogen gas. The great Orion nebula is an example of such a cloud. (See Plate XI.) It is visible because it is illuminated by neighboring stars. There is not much variety or much order in this cloud. Hydrogen atoms are moving at random, occasionally colliding with one another.

The cloud undergoes slow changes under the influence of gravity. It is true that the gravitational attraction between hydrogen atoms is extremely weak because of their small mass. If the cloud is very large, however, the combined gravitational effect of many atoms becomes important. Over long periods of time groupings do occur, and such a grouping represents a stronger center of attraction than a single atom. It therefore attracts more atoms and becomes an even stronger center, which in turn forces more and more atoms into its region. Finally one or a few large, dense clusters of hydrogen atoms are formed, and they grow bigger still until they have attracted most of the material of the cloud.

The gravitational force goes on pulling the atoms together, so that the cluster becomes smaller and denser. The atoms "fall" toward the center under the pull of gravity. During this fall they acquire speed; when they get into dense regions, they will collide with other atoms and transmit the energy of their motion to the rest of the material. So the contraction of the cluster causes the atoms to move faster and faster and collide with each other. Gravitational energy is transformed into irregular heat motion. The gas in the cluster gets denser and hotter.

The First Stage of a Star. The temperature rises by gravitational contraction, and after some time reaches a level where the collision energies are beyond the stability level of the hydrogen atom. Then the atoms are lifted to excited quantum states; when they return to their ground states, light is produced. The characteristic radiation of

Plate XI. The great nebula in Orion.

hydrogen is emitted. At this stage the object becomes luminous—we see radiating gas.

The gravitational contraction does not stop at this point; it squeezes the atoms closer together and raises the temperature higher and higher. A stage is reached where the atoms in the center of the object get so close to each other that the electron patterns interfere; the temperature becomes so high that electrons are torn off. Enormous amounts of light are emitted by the object; it is no longer pure hydrogen light but light of all wave lengths, produced by widely moving free electrons and tightly squeezed atoms. The cluster becomes a real star in its first stage of development. (See Figures 58 and 59.)

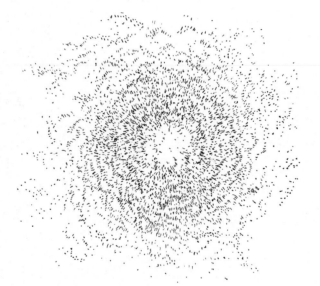

Figure 58. Hydrogen gas cluster.

The Second Stage of a Star. Gravitational contraction would go on indefinitely making the star hotter and denser were it not for a new process that sets in when the temperature becomes very high, so high that nuclear processes are induced. We expect that this must happen in the center of the star, where the temperatures are highest. When the temperature reaches the values needed for nuclear burning of hydrogen, about five billion degrees, the second stage in the life of the star begins.

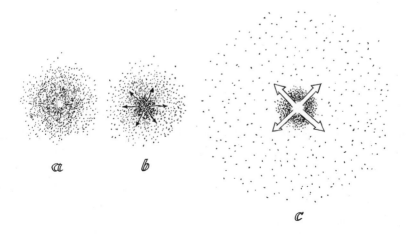

Figure 59. The first three stages of a star. (a) Hydrogen gas ball. (b) Hydrogen burning takes place at the center and develops counterpressure. Heat flows outwards from the center. (c) Red giant: Helium burning at the center. Enormous heat radiates from the center. It disperses the outside material over large sphere.

Nuclear burning of hydrogen was described in Chapter Seven. We recapitulate: Nuclei of hydrogen atoms—protons, long since freed of their electrons—hit each other at high temperature and form diprotons, which become deuterons by radioactive transmutation. Then pairs of deuterons fuse and form helium nuclei. (See Figure 49, Chapter Seven.) This is the nuclear fire lighted by the heat of compression in the center of the star. It produces enormous energies, and the corresponding counterpressure generated at the center stops the gravitational collapse. The contraction ceases, and for a long time afterward the star remains of the same size.

Hydrogen burning is a slow but efficient process. The heat produced by this fire works its way to the surface and maintains the brilliance of the star. It supplies the energy needed for constant emission of light from the stellar surface into space. It keeps the star going for a long time. Several billion years pass by before the hydrogen in the hot region at the center is depleted and turned into helium.

The Third Stage of a Star. When most of the hydrogen is exhausted in the central region, the hydrogen fire comes to an end and the counterpressure which had prevented gravitational contraction subsides. Then gravity does its work again, and the star contracts further. This is always connected with a rise in temperature, since the atoms "fall" inward and gain speed. There comes a moment then when the center reaches the temperature, about 100 billion degrees, at which helium starts burning. This is the beginning of the third stage of the star. The helium nuclear fire comes from the formation of carbon in a fusion of three helium nuclei (as we saw in Chapter Seven. The helium fire burns rather fast and produces more heat than slow-burning hydrogen fire. The pressure of the heat at the center not only stops the contraction, but pushes the rest of the material of the star away from the center. The star then consists of a very hot and dense center, where the nuclear burning goes on, surrounded by a giant sphere of very dilute material. Most of this dilute material is the original hydrogen that escaped burning in the second stage because it was not at the hot center. Such stars are called red giants; they are red because the outer material is so far away from the center that it glows reddishly and not with white light, as it did in the second stage.

Development is rapid in the red-giant stage. Soon the temperature at the center reaches a point at which helium nuclei are brought in close contact with the newly formed carbon nuclei. This contact produces a nuclear fire resulting in oxygen formation. The oxygen nucleus is a combination of four helium nuclei. Further increase of temperature allows the formation of combinations of five, six, or more helium nuclei, neon, magnesium, silicon, sulfur, etc.

At this stage the temperature in the middle of the star is so high that the center becomes a hot, element-producing oven. Many other types of nuclei are formed besides those that are combinations of helium nuclei. Some nuclei originate when these combinations collide with a proton and form new units. Others are formed when neutrons are added to previously formed nuclei. The neutrons needed for this process come from energetic nuclear collisions in which they were chipped off from other nuclei, and they drift around until picked up. This way many nuclear types are produced; some have a surplus of neutrons or protons and hence are radioactive. These transform into new, more stable varieties.

Let us keep in mind that this nuclei-producing activity is restricted to the very center of the star. The rest of the star is much too cool for any nuclear fire. Consequently most of the star material remains hydrogen and serves as an immense container for the productive oven in the center.

Explosion and Rebirth. We do not know very much about what happens when the third stage is over and the nuclear fire subsides because of the exhaustion of fuel at the center. There are many theories of star evolution after the third stage. It is probable that the star contracts to a very small size with extremely high temperatures, and becomes what is called a white dwarf. For our purpose this further development is no longer so interesting, since it does not lead to any new element formation. One thing, however, is important for us: At the end of the third stage, when the nuclear fire is burned out, a few stars, not all of them, undergo a violent rearrangement of matter that results in a tremendous explosion. These explosions are seen from time to time when a giant star suddenly becomes extremely bright. We call such a phenomenon a supernova. When this explosion occurs, most of the star material is hurled out in interstellar space to mix with the original hydrogen gas. When new stars are formed in a region where a supernova explosion has occurred, the hydrogen gas is no longer pure. There are traces of other elements mixed into it; hence a star developing from such gas contains from the outset a variety of elements.

The star explosion is a relatively rare event. Probably only a few per cent of the stars undergo this violent stage. It is a very important event, however, since the nuclei formed in the hot center of the star are spread all over space. It is important for another reason: There are certain heavy atomic nuclei possessing nuclear structures that could not have been produced even in the hottest star centers. Gold, lead, and uranium are examples. A star explosion creates conditions of very intense nuclear collisions in which even the most complicated nuclear structures could originate. Therefore it is highly probable that these heavy nuclei were created during the process of explosion and then scattered over vast space.

A new "second generation" of stars is formed of original hydrogen gases into which star explosions have mixed their material. The development of these second generation stars is not very different from the first-generation stars, since the admixture of non-hydrogen material is very weak. The gas out of which they develop is still mainly hydrogen.

The Sun is an example of a star that originated from a hydrogen cloud contaminated with remnants of an exploding star. It is now in its second stage of development, burning hydrogen to helium. This slow and regular nuclear fire supplies the energy with which the Sun has radiated its warm light steadily for several billion years. Had the Sun originated from a pure hydrogen cloud, it would contain nothing but hydrogen and helium. The Sun does consist mostly of hydrogen and helium, but when we investigate light emitted from the Sun's surface, we find traces of other elements, and these elements testify to the fact that the Sun is from a "later generation" of stars, that the material of which it is made had been in another, earlier star.

THE CREATION OF THE EARTH

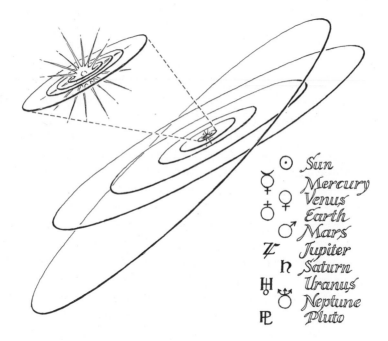

Figure 60. Orbits (and symbols) of planets.

When the Sun was formed from the original contaminated hydrogen cloud, some special process must have occurred that placed little chunks of matter in orbits circling around the Sun. We know that the Sun is surrounded by nine planets, which are very much smaller than the Sun itself (Figure 60). The genesis of these little chunks is of great importance to us, since we live on one of them.

We have only very vague ideas of the mechanism that brought these planets into being. One way to imagine their origin would be this: When the gas cloud contracted and formed the star, small bits of cloud must have been left behind. They gathered together by gravity and formed the sub-units which now circle the Sun as planets. Originally these left-behind parts consisted, of course, of the same material as the rest—that is, mostly hydrogen with a small admixture of heavier elements. When the parts gathered together into planets, a separation of elements set in. The planets, especially the small ones, consist mainly of heavier elements and contain only a little hydrogen and helium. There are two reasons for this. First, the heavier atoms are more strongly attracted than the light ones; since the gravitational pull of the small subunits was not very strong, the light elements, such as hydrogen, escaped the pull to a large extent and drifted away. Second, because of the small size of the subunits, their gravitational contraction did not produce high temperatures, as it did in the stars. Hence the atoms formed molecules, and some molecules aggregated into liquids and solids. Those elements forming gases, however, in part escaped and in part formed layers of gas on the surfaces of the planets, the atmospheres. The planets (especially the smaller ones) consist mainly of substances that form good solids, such as iron and rock.

In other words, during the formation of the smaller planets such as our Earth most of the light hydrogen atoms escaped, and what was left was mostly the material that had been added to the original hydrogen cloud in a previous star explosion. The composition of our Earth is a consequence of the contamination of the original gas cloud of the solar system. The process of formation of the Earth eliminated most of the hydrogen and retained the heavier elements, which had their origin in the center of a previous star. This does not mean that no hydrogen was left on Earth. Only hydrogen gas escaped from the planet. The hydrogen atoms that formed molecules of liquids or solids with other atoms were retained. For example, a large number of hydrogen atoms formed water molecules with oxygen and thus stayed on Earth in the form of water or ice.

We now can trace the history of matter on Earth from its origin in a pure hydrogen cloud to its present state. The original cloud concentrated into stars, and at least one star must have exploded. The material of the explosion was spread into other hydrogen clouds, which again formed stars, and one of these stars is the Sun. During the formation of the Sun small amounts of material aggregated in the immediate neighborhood and formed planets, which retained mostly the heavier elements. Hence everything we see around us here—the carbon in the paper, the lead in the pencil, the silicon in the rock, the iron in the car—came from the hot center of an exploded star, and was assembled billions of years later on our planet Earth.

The development of this paper and pencil, the rock and the car, began with simple hydrogen gas consisting only of protons and electrons. Gravitational compression establishes conditions in the center of the star, where protons are squeezed into the quantum patterns of atomic nuclei after some of the protons are changed over to neutrons in the radioactive process. New and more differentiated units are created—the atomic nuclei. They represent an orderly arrangement in contrast to the random regime in the hydrogen gas. More of these units are formed during the explosion.

Afterward, when the nuclei are expelled into cool space, they gather electrons around them which no longer move at random; they fall into the quantum patterns typical for the atomic species to which the nucleus belongs. More order is created; more specific units appear, the atoms of the various elements. So far these new atoms are spread all over space in random fashion. They represent only an insignificant percentage of the random gas in space which still is mostly hydrogen.

Later on, however, when another star develops from this gas, the new atomic species are segregated from hydrogen into the planets. Because of the low temperature on the planets further differentiation occurs. Molecules are formed, and they aggregate into liquids and solids on the surfaces of the planets. So we see how, in this development, nature steps down the quantum ladder, rung by rung. It starts with protons and neutrons, forming nuclei in the center of stars, then atoms in space, and finally molecules and crystals on a few planets where the temperatures are appropriate.

In this development only a very small part of the original hydrogen is transformed into other elements. Enormous amounts of hydrogen are needed to create the conditions under which a tiny part turns into more complex units. Stars must assemble, explode, and reassemble in order to turn a negligibly small part of the original stuff into the variegated substances and materials which we find on Earth.

How long did this development take? As we learned in Chapter

Two, the solar system originated about 4.5 billion years ago. The explosion of the stars that delivered the different atomic species must have occurred earlier; there is some indication that this happened about seven to ten billion years ago. The life span of an average star is estimated to be about ten billion years. It must have been twenty billion years ago, therefore, when the first hydrogen cloud started forming the star which made our elements. Much time and much material were needed to create the substance of our world.

THE DEVELOPMENT OF LIFE

The Beginnings. We have followed the evolution of our world from the hydrogen cloud to the development of stars with planets. The planets are an agglomeration of matter in a more "advanced" form; they consist mostly of elements more complex than hydrogen. The Earth, for example, is made up of many elements. The bulk consists of heavy metals, mostly iron; the outer layers are rock and minerals; on the surface there is much water. The outside is covered by a layer of gas, the atmosphere.

The remainder of our story of evolution takes place beneath this protective layer of gas, on the surface of the Earth. It is a story of further differentiation of matter, of the formation and propagation of complex units of matter which make up the living world on Earth, but any statements concerning the origin and the early stages of life must be very tentative, since that origin occurred under very different conditions.

In facing this problem, as in facing the previous one of the development of stars and planets, we are in the position of explorers who are trying to draw a map of an unknown continent. Their knowledge is patchy, they have seen only small stretches of the coast line, followed a reach of water here, found a river farther inland. When drawing the map they must rely on their imagination to fill in the unknown parts of the coast line, and they tentatively assume that the reach of water and the river are two parts of the same. It is the best they can do. A later map will show that they simplified and distorted the picture enormously and that, after all, their two bodies of water were not the same river. But generally, despite the errors, the explorers' outlines will be recognizable.

Our knowledge of the development of the world is patchy too. We are forced to use our imagination at almost any step to fill in many unknown stretches. Many things I am saying here will turn out later to be wrong. Still there is good reason to think that the general trend of events is correctly conceived today.

Let us try to look at our planet as it was three billion years ago. (See Figure 61.) On the whole it was not very different from its

Figure 61. Primitive Earth before life appeared.

present state. Its orbit around the Sun and its internal constitution were much the same as now. Only on the surface was there a difference. It was all rock and water, nothing else. The atmosphere contained nitrogen, carbon dioxide, methane, ammonia, but no oxygen. Oxygen reacts strongly with most materials and forms stable chemical compounds. Hence it can exist in the atmosphere only if it is constantly reproduced by some process in which it is liberated from chemical compounds. We saw in Chapter Seven that this happens today in the chlorophyll of green plants, but the plants did not exist in the early stages.

The Earth is exposed to the light of the Sun, which furnishes a continuous supply of heat and keeps the Earth's surface warm. The distance between the Sun and the Earth is such that the temperature over most parts of the Earth's surface stays between zero and one hundred degrees centigrade, and water to a great extent can exist in its liquid form. This circumstance is most important for the further history of the Earth, since liquid water is the best receptacle for many chemical substances and allows them to react easily with each other.

The absence of oxygen had an important effect: The ultraviolet light from the Sun penetrated freely to the Earth's surface, whereas today it is absorbed almost completely by oxygen in the uppermost layers of air. Ultraviolet light is chemically active. It breaks the molecular bonds between atoms and then permits them to combine in different ways. As a consequence, it produces new chemical compounds from old ones. We therefore can assume that solar radiation produced a variety of new chemical compounds which were not present before. Among these new compounds there certainly were also some of the molecules that play a rôle in living structures, such as sugar, nucleotides and amino acids. The formation of these molecules must have been a very slow process. The ultraviolet light first had to decompose molecules containing the necessary atoms, and then chance brought the atoms together in the right positions to form the new molecules. Simple structures must have been formed more frequently than complicated ones, because it is much more probable that a few atoms would get into the right position than that many of them would. Alcohol and sugar were formed by sunlight in much larger quantities than amino acids and nucleotides.

The formation was slow, but over many millions of years these substances did accumulate. When formed at the surface of water, they sank to lower layers and were protected against break-up by ultraviolet sunlight. Today such accumulation would be impossible; amino acids or nucleotides would be quickly incorporated in living organisms or decomposed by oxidation with free oxygen in the atmosphere. The sterile conditions of the early periods permitted the slow accumulation. Thus it came about that the waters on Earth slowly began to contain small quantities of sugar and similar compounds and even smaller quantities of amino acids and nucleotides.

In the great oceans these molecules got lost easily and strayed far apart from each other. In smaller ponds or puddles, however, the concentration may have become not inconsiderable. Some nucleotides might even have joined together and formed a small chain of nucleic acid, and some amino acids might have joined to form a protein chain. Smaller bodies of water, therefore, must have contained a few short chains of nucleic acids and proteins. But the chains that are formed in chance encounters are not the chains that play a rôle in life. They are accidental combinations without any special significance or special chemical activity. One day one type of protein would have been formed; the next day another type.

The nucleic acids formed by the accidental joining of nucleotides had more lasting effects. We saw in Chapter Eight that a nucleic acid chain of the DNA type can reproduce itself exactly by dividing into two halves, and that each of the halves then collects the correct nucleotides for the build-up of two identical full chains. Therefore if a nucleic acid chain is put into a medium containing nucleotides, the chain may produce more and more replicas of itself until all the nucleotides are used up. So if one chain should be formed by accidental encounter, this chain then would induce all other nucleotides in the neighborhood into forming chains of the same kind. Nucleic acids are able to produce replicas in an environment where nucleotides are available. In many respects this property is the basis of life, since it allows a complicated structure to reproduce itself under favorable conditions.

Nucleic acids can do more than just reproduce themselves. We learned in Chapter Seven that they are the templates bringing together amino acids in a fixed order in which they join to a chain and form a certain protein. Probably every nucleic acid chain (or spiral staircase, if it is the DNA type) acts as a mold for one or more proteins. Therefore when a certain type of nucleic acid is present in a liquid where there are also amino acids, it will make the latter combine into protein chains; it will produce those proteins of which it is a template.

Hence, according to our ideas, whenever a number of nucleotides in our puddle of water joined by accident to a nucleic acid chain, this chain then not only formed replicas of itself, but also induced the formation of certain proteins. All nearby nucleotides and amino acids then would be used up to form nucleic acids and proteins of a type determined by the accidental formation of the first nucleic acid.

For two reasons this process must have been a very slow one. First, amino acids and nucleotides were few and far apart in the waters. Most of the molecules formed by the ultraviolet light were simpler ones, such as sugar or alcohol, and were not usable for nucleic acid or proton formation. Second, energy is necessary for the construction of chains. In this primitive stage only heat energy or radiation energy was available, and neither of them would have been very effective for this purpose. Nevertheless, many reproductions of nucleic acids must have occurred in the millions of years between the creation of the planets and the beginning of life.

A CHANCE HAPPENING

Imagine what happened when, by chance, one of these accidental encounters produced a special nucleic acid, the one that is the template for those proteins which make nucleotides from sugar and ammonia. Then the production of replicas would have been immensely accelerated, since the proteins formed would have used all available sugar and ammonia and would have produced a much larger supply of nucleotides for nucleic acid replication. The body of water in which this happened would have been richer in nucleic acids than any other.

This special body of water would be distinguished in other respects too. There would be many more nucleotides in it than in the others, and chance combinations of nucleic acids would occur much more frequently than otherwise. What is more important, the special nucleic acid, the template of the nucleotide-producing protein, would from time to time catch more nucleotides and thus add to its chain. Such an increase would not remain a single event but would reappear in each replica of the nucleic acid. Additions to the chain are products of chance and therefore, in most cases, would not produce templates for important proteins. But in the course of many years it might have happened that in one of these favored puddles of water a longer nucleic acid was formed, one capable of producing more than one "useful" protein.

At that state of development the useful proteins are these:

a.   One producing nucleotides from sugar, phosphate, and ammonia.
b.   One producing amino acids from sugar, phosphate, and ammonia.
c.   One that can "burn" a sugar molecule—that is, one that can transfer the energy contained in the sugar into those energy carriers which we met under the name of ATP molecules in Chapter Seven.
d.   One serving as a coat or skin for the nucleic acid, a skin which has small pores that let simple chemicals through, but keep chain molecules inside.
e.   One that forms special molecules capable of synthesizing sugar with the help of sunlight. (Chlorophyll is an example.)[1]

Let us now discuss the effects of these useful proteins. We have described already the great usefulness of protein (a) for nucleic acid formation. The protein (b) would strongly increase the amino acid supply, which previously was furnished only by the slow method of ultraviolet-light production. This protein (b) contribution obviously would enhance the formation of any kind of protein when a nucleic acid template was available.

The protein (c) accelerates all chain-building processes, since it provides suitable energy carriers which help to link one molecule to the next in the chain. Before these ATP energy carriers were available, the energy needed for the linking was supplied by heat, in a very unreliable and slow way to build a chain.

The protein (d) serves a most significant purpose. Before the formation of this protein, the body of water acts more or less as one unit. The multiplication of nucleic acids makes use of the total supply of nucleotides. For example, in that favored body of water where nucleotide-producing proteins were formed, the nucleotides would be used for multiplication by any kind of nucleic acid in that pond and not just by the one that was the template for the particular protein and therefore responsible for its formation. That specific nucleic acid, therefore, does not enjoy the advantages of its talent to the exclusion of other nucleic acids. They all will multiply and use up the raw materials. But if the effective nucleic acid also can pro-

[1] We have simplified the situation by pretending that one protein only is needed for each of these tasks. In fact each task needs a whole system of several special proteins, but the trend of thought here would hold.

duce a skin, the productive protein and its products will be kept close, and the products will be available exclusively to this specific nucleic acid. Hence this one alone would be able to produce many replicas, and it would develop very much more rapidly than the others. Not only would the others be deprived of the increased supply of nucleotides, but the skin would keep the building materials close at hand when they were needed.

With the formation of a nucleic acid that can produce proteins of the type (a), (b), (c), and (d) life has started to exist. Here we have something closely resembling a bacterial cell. When such a unit is found in a puddle of water with sugar and other simple chemicals, it actually lives. Amino acids and nucleotides are pro-

Figure 62. The oldest known living forms from about 1600 million years ago, resembled algae. From microphotographs by Professor E. S. Barghoorn of Harvard University.

duced within the unit: the former are put together to the necessary proteins by the nucleic acid serving as a template; the nucleotides are used when the nucleic acid forms a replica of itself. When the unit becomes too big, it will burst, and each separate nucleic acid will form its own unit again. This bursting and reforming might have been the first and simplest way of cell division. It was a very wasteful one, since many substances were lost in the process. Nowadays a cell has a much better way to divide without loss of material.

Even this advanced chemical unit could not go on multiplying itself forever, since it "fed" upon the simple chemicals such as sugar, phosphates, and ammonia. There was and is no shortage of phosphates and ammonia on Earth. They are simple low-energy compounds available in large quantities. But the supply of sugar was not unlimited. Sugar, a chemical compound of "high energy," was made by ultraviolet light in small quantities only. When the sugar supply of a body of water was exhausted, our units no longer could multiply. The ones destroyed by external causes, such as collisions, by exposure to too much radiation or loss of proteins during the primitive division process, etc., no longer could be replaced, and the units would die out.

So we can see why the protein (e) is of such enormous importance. A nucleic acid which, in addition to proteins (a) to (d), also can produce protein (e) is in a very privileged position: The unit to which it belongs depends no longer upon the sugar contained in the body of water. It produces its own sugar by using ordinary (not ultraviolet) sunlight as an energy source, and it needs only very simple low-energy chemical substances, such as carbon dioxide and water, for this process.

It is important to realize that all the five types of proteins are doing is no more than an acceleration of natural processes. For example, proteins (a) and (b) produce nucleotides and amino acids from simpler chemicals, a process which already has occurred in the water, but at a vastly slower rate. Protein (c) supplies energy in ready-made packages, but energy already was available in the form of heat, which is rather ineffective. Protein (d) forms a small private body of water for each nucleic acid and so increases the rate of chemical reactions enormously. Protein (e) creates a substance that produces sugar with the help of sunlight in a much more efficient way than it was done by ultraviolet light. Thus proteins are extremely efficient catalyzers of natural processes.

The Evolution of Life. We now have arrived at a point where things are ready for a great development. Let us summarize the situation: At some places on Earth certain combinations of chain molecules have originated. These combinations have the remarkable property of being able to reproduce themselves, if the raw material is available in the form of simple molecules. This reproduction is determined by a special chain molecule, the nucleic acid. In fact, it is only the nucleic acid chain that actually reproduces itself.

Each new replica of this molecule induces the formation of the same proteins and thus creates a new replica of the previous unit.

Once such combinations originate, they are bound to accumulate in large numbers. In particular, those combinations will multiply rapidly which, in their reproduction, make efficient use of simple chemical compounds as raw material, because that form of raw material is plentiful on Earth.

Further development is based upon the interplay of two factors. One is the self-reproduction of the units; the other is the "mutation" of the structure of the nucleic acid. We use the term "mutation" for the following phenomenon: In the course of self-reproduction it is bound to happen that sometimes the replication of the nucleic acid chain is not exact. Changes will occur from time to time.

The changes we may expect will be of two kinds. First, errors occur in the process of replication. The new nucleic acid sometimes is not exactly the same as the old one. If the new form becomes unable to produce the necessary proteins, the unit in which the change has occurred will cease to develop. If, however, the new form of nucleic acid produces the necessary proteins in spite of the change, the alterations will be repeated in each replica, and, therefore, they will be maintained from then on in the progeny.

Second, nucleic acids may acquire additional groups of nucleotides and thus increase their length. After all, the chains of the first nucleic acids were quite short; they served as templates for a very few proteins only. Whenever a few nucleotides are added by some chance, these additions are reproduced from then on in the replicas. In most cases these additions are valueless for protein production. Over very long periods, however, it is bound to happen from time to time that they give rise to a better protein, or that the extension of the nucleic acid can produce an additional new protein that will help to use more efficiently the raw materials available for reproduction. Whenever this happens, this new type of unit soon replaces the old one, since it multiplies faster and therefore uses up for its own replication all available material.[2]

[2] There is a process to build up larger chains of nucleic acids, and probably it happens frequently when a chain reproduces a replica of itself. The replica sometimes does not separate completely from the original molecule; the ends might still stick to each other. Then a chain of double length is formed. This new chain cannot produce more proteins than the old one did; it produces the same ones but twice over. However, it is less endangered when changes occur in further replications. Whenever a change does occur, there still remains the other half intact, and it can produce the necessary proteins. Hence changes can be transmitted to the next genera-

It might also happen that the new proteins allow the units to multiply under different external conditions. For example, the old unit multiplies best in warm water, the new one in colder water; or the old one in the deep parts of the water, the new one in the shallow regions near the shores. Then the new types will not displace the old ones, but they will populate regions on Earth where the new conditions exist.

Here we have the process of natural selection. It is bound to set in when certain units have the capability of reproducing themselves and when the master plan of this reproduction undergoes arbitrary changes. These two factors, self-reproduction and mutation, work hand in hand. If the reproduction is unaffected by the changes, nothing much happens; the changes are bequeathed to the progeny. If multiplication is reduced by the changes, the units afflicted will die out; if the mutations give rise to units which reproduce more efficiently, these units will replace the old ones. Thus a slow development goes on toward units that are better adapted for multiplication under the existing conditions.

There is a characteristic trend in this development—the units are bound to become more and more complicated. They lose the simple features they had at the beginning of life's history. Most changes are steps toward higher differentiation, toward longer chains of nucleic acid, which produce more proteins with more specialized tasks. Hence from the moment when units exist that can form replicas of themselves, a development toward more and more complicated units is bound to start. Better adaption to external conditions leads almost always to more complicated units.

This development is very similar to the development of our automobiles. Every year the designers try to improve the cars with small additions here and there. The machine becomes increasingly complicated. No doubt it would be possible to produce a much better, less complicated, car but only at the labor of redesigning it in every respect. Man can redesign automobiles, but nature cannot redesign in the process of natural selection. In nature the development can proceed only by an accumulation of a small change here, another there, occurring in the nucleic acid master plan. Nature cannot start again from scratch. It can only add to the previous develop-

---

tions although the changes, without this doubling, might have led to death. After several such mutations, the doubled chain would be able to produce new proteins in addition to those produced by the original nucleic acid.

ment. Therefore progress in nature is nearly always achieved by going over to a more complicated unit.

Here is a mechanism with a truly remarkable quality. It provides a possibility for nature to improve itself, to "construct" more and more complicated structures, and to do this in a quite "natural" way without violating any of the fundamental laws of physics and chemistry and without having recourse to any pre-established plan. This process is all the more remarkable since, more often than not, we find in the inorganic world the opposite trend: Complicated structures decay into less complicated ones; order goes toward disorder. The build-up process is possible only because of the phenomenon of self-replication. It automatically multiplies a more complicated structure if and when the structure is better adapted to its environment.[3]

Let us look now at the development that has occurred by natural selection. We start with a rudimentary plant cell; it contains the necessary proteins which make amino acids and nucleotides from sugar, phosphate, and ammonia, and with chlorophyll, which produces sugar with the help of sunlight. Most important, it contains the nucleic acid that acts as template for the fabrication of all the proteins.

In the course of further development mutations add many more steps to the nucleic acid. The acid now provides the templates for proteins giving rise to a cell of a more complicated structure, much more advanced and better organized than the first rudimentary cells. Indeed, the process of cell division has become so much better organized that none of the cell substances is lost in the division. An elaborate mechanism initiated and governed by the actions of suitable proteins did in fact achieve this evolution.

Nor did growth stop there. Obviously more growth and multiplication could be achieved if several cells acted together as one multicellular unit. The unit can work more efficiently if the functions are divided among different cells. Some cells can serve as framework, some can collect the raw materials from the water or

---

[3] This trend toward complication in living structures is not in disagreement with the over-all law of thermodynamics, which says that the total entropy (measure of disorder) must increase steadily. The increase of "order" in a living structure is always accompanied by a decrease of order in the sustaining physical environment. This balance is most important in the build-up of organic molecules in plants, which is done with the help of sunlight. For every molecule constructed, so much light energy is absorbed. This light energy was produced with a large loss of "order" in the solar material that emitted it.

the ground, and others grow where the sunlight is intense, and serve mainly as sugar producers. By adding one complication to the other, units such as our present plants were developed, consisting of millions of cells for many different purposes. In time a green blanket of plant life covered the Earth. (See Figure 63.)

Figure 63. A green blanket of plant life covered the Earth.

Once this cover of plants was established, new possibilities of life arose. Two essential things had changed. First, there was now available a plentiful supply of sugar, nucleotides, and amino acids in the plants, a supply that renewed itself continuously by multiplication. Second, the sugar production by chlorophyll set free an enormous amount of oxygen gas. The atmosphere of the Earth slowly filled with oxygen, and the oxygen remained in the air because all losses from oxidation and other chemical reactions were constantly replenished.

Let us look at the effects of these two most important changes. Before the spread of plant life, it was most useful for a living unit to contain chlorophyll because the unit then could produce its own sugar. Sugar, because it was produced most inefficiently by ultraviolet radiation, was very scarce on Earth. After the spread of plants over the Earth, however, sugar was plentifully available in the plants. The same is true to an even higher degree with respect to amino acids or nucleotides. These more complicated molecules were in very short supply before the spread of plants, but afterward the surface of the Earth was covered with them.

Consequently at that stage of development living units unable to produce their own sugar or amino acid needs could exist. They could develop easily and multiply by "feeding" upon the supply of these substances in plants. This fact has most interesting consequences. Before the plant cover, any mutation that destroyed the nucleic acid's ability to produce amino acids and chlorophyll would make it impossible for the unit to multiply efficiently, and the changed units would die out. But after the plant cover originated, such changes were not so dangerous; the unit could go on multiplying by thriving on plant supply. Therefore many changes which earlier would have died out now were able to survive and multiply. This is why, after the plant cover, new kinds of living species developed; we call them animals. Freed from the necessity of producing fundamental chemicals, such as amino acids, nucleotides and chlorophyll, these new units developed their nucleic acid master plan in new directions. Multicellular units originated where the different cells had other functions too, such as locomotion and sensitivity to light and sound. They could move, see, and hear.

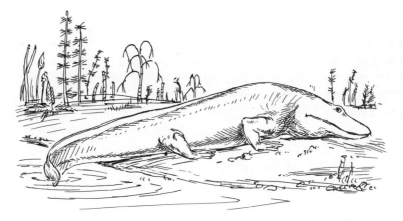

Figure 64. Restoration of small Pennsylvanian amphibian (diplovertebron).

We must keep in mind how slow this development has been. It stretches over one or two billion years. The changes come about by an accumulation of mutation effects. It takes a long time before an accidental change or increase of the nucleic acid chain leads to a useful addition to the master plan. However, a new and more efficient way of development originated when two units united before replication and made use of a mixture of their nucleic acids in the replicas. This system, the sexual replication, has the great advantage of combining new, successful trends that occur in each individual. It accelerates the development of better-adapted units. This is the reason it is today the most common form of replication among the more complicated units.

It is a most important fact in the evolution of living structures that acquired properties are not inherited. A change in body structure inflicted upon an individual will never be inherited by its offspring. We can cut off the tails of all members of a group of animals and keep cutting off the tails of the offspring, but the newly born will always have tails. The reason is obvious. A change inflicted on the body structure has no effect on the nucleic acids in the cells which contain the blueprint of the new individuals. As long as the tail is planned in the blueprint, it will develop in the offspring, regardless of what has happened to the parents' tails.

Let us return to the second change that plant life introduced— oxygen in the atmosphere. Recall that the building up of proteins and nucleic acids needs energy. The energy was provided by certain proteins which can regulate the burning of sugar to carbon dioxide and water and can store the energy in small packages within the ATP molecules. The burning of sugar without ample supply of oxygen is not easy. There are oxygen atoms contained in the sugar molecule itself; they can be used for the burning. This type of burning, which uses the oxygen in the sugar, is called fermentation; it is an inefficient way of getting energy from sugar. When free oxygen became available in the atmosphere, it was much easier to burn sugar in the cell and to store energy in the ATP molecules. New units originated that made use of atmospheric oxygen in their energy production. This led not only to a much faster growth of new cells, but also created an energy surplus within the units which could be used for moving parts of the unit. Muscles were developed, and they caused the extremities to move and to perform work for locomotion and for gathering up food.

In those large multicellular units we call animals, the oxygen of the air cannot penetrate easily into the body cells. Therefore the following change in the master plan led to much better-adapted units: There developed a system of arteries in which a liquid containing special red cells is pumped throughout the body. These red cells absorb free oxygen easily and transport it to all the body cells, which need it for energy production. The absorption of oxygen occurs in certain tissues—the lungs—which are constantly filled with fresh air. Thus the animals with blood circulation could make much better use of oxygen for their energy supply.

But the greatest step forward in this trend for better coping with environment was the development of the nervous system. This is a special combination of interlocking cells capable of transmitting stimuli from one part of the unit to the other. By these special cells, sense organs, through connecting neurons, could be made to affect muscles to co-ordinate locomotion with light or sound seen or heard by the unit. As a result, the units could react upon changes in the environment in many ways that are most useful for the protection of the individual and for the acquisition of food. The structure could move toward light; it could recognize food by its smell or its shape; it could avoid danger by moving away or by protecting itself when large objects approached. Our unit acquires what we call a "behavior."

The development of a nervous system was so useful and effective that any mutation or sexual combination leading to a larger nervous system gave rise to increasingly successful units. Thus a continuous evolution towards an increase in nerve cells began and led to the formation of a brain. This organ is an accumulation of a large number of interconnected nerve cells capable of storing the effects of the stimuli which the unit has received. The storage was the beginning of what we call memory. An action that previously has had good results with respect to food intake or avoidance of pain is kept in memory and repeated readily if similar circumstances recur. Obviously the ability to "remember" such situations was an enormous asset for our units and helped their struggle for survival under difficult conditions. It supplied the ability to learn from experience.

Such memory and learning mechanisms need not be very complicated. One can easily construct a machine with a "nervous system" that remembers past situations and determines its actions on that basis by means of modern electronic equipment. A system of interlocking nerve cells is in many ways equivalent to a system of interconnected electronic vacuum tubes or transistors. A machine with a few thousand vacuum tubes can perform most impressive acts of remembering situations and avoiding them later on. But in fact the brain of even an insect is a more complicated device. It contains ten to a hundred thousand nerve cells. The human brain has as many as ten billion.

The event of brain formation is an important step in the development of life. Before this event a living unit and its reactions to the outside world are completely determined by chemical structure. After the event the reactions of the unit depend not only upon its structure but also upon its previous experience. Its behavior is determined not by the nucleic acid master plan alone, but also by what the unit has experienced in the course of its life. The individual unit is formed not only by its biological development from the nucleic acid, but also by the effects of the environment on its behavior.

In the course of the development of the brain the rôle of memory and acquired experience slowly became more important. Not only do nerves transmit stimuli from one part of the body to the other; when they are suitably interlaced, they also can store information and transform it into concepts which later on may cause new actions. The enormous advantage of this mechanism has put a high premium on the development of complicated nerve-cell assemblies. Nucleic acids that acquired chains capable of stimulating the growth of those assemblies led to the development of successful living units. The animals spread over the Earth.

Let us keep in mind, however, that behavior based on learning and memory is only a very small part of the behavior pattern. Most of the behavior of primitive animals is predetermined as it develops according to the nucleic acid master plan. It is inherited, as we say. Birds build their nests, feed their young, and migrate to the South in the winter by instinct. These behavior patterns are not learned; they are inborn. The nerve complexes causing these actions are already preformed in the growing body. The reactions acquired by learning are few. Birds learn certain ways of twittering; some higher animals learn certain hunting tricks. Most important reactions of animals are inborn, however, as is shown by the fact that in most species newly born animals are able to live normally when raised without contact with their like. Hence both the body structure of each individual and its social behavior as well are governed by the code within the cell.

Shape and behavior are predetermined in the nucleic acid. They are repeated in each new generation and change only if a mutation has occurred. The behavior changes as slowly as the body structure. Ants and bees have the same social structure as long as they exist as the same species, and this existence extends over many thousands of generations. The same is true of higher animals.

The Evolution of Man. In our tale of evolution we have reached the point where something new is beginning to develop, brought about by a simple increase in quantity of the cells making up the nervous system. It happens often in the material world that an increase in quantity at a certain point gives rise to deep qualitative changes.

Let us look at an example of quality from quantity. An open vessel filled with water is enclosed in a room. When the temperature is below the boiling point, an equilibrium is established in which a certain number of water molecules per second evaporate from the surface, and the same number per second return from the water vapor in the air and condense at the surface. The water in the vessel remains seemingly undisturbed, in equilibrium with the (moist) air. When we raise the temperature but still keep it below the boiling point, there is only a quantitative change. There are just more molecules per second leaving and returning to the surface. If the number of molecules evaporating and condensing per second goes on increasing, however, a point will be reached where the returning molecules can no longer keep up with the leaving ones. The temperature at which the evaporation cannot be compensated for by condensation has arrived, and the water is transformed completely into vapor. In other words, it boils away. To the onlooker it may seem that at the boiling temperature something special happens to the water. This is, in fact, not so; evaporation does occur also at lower temperatures. The decisive change is in the relation of the water to the surrounding air. At the boiling point the air can no longer replenish the molecules lost by evaporation; so the evaporation, which was "harmless" to the water below the boiling point, "destroys" the water above this point.

We can observe a similar phenomenon in a solution of salt in water. If the concentration of salt is below the saturation point, the solution looks clear and no deposit is formed. Actually, however, the salt molecules do hit the walls of the vessel and form very tiny agglomerations, but the deposit is dissolved immediately. If the concentration of the solution is increased beyond the saturation point (e.g., by boiling off some water), the speed of formation of deposit surpasses the speed of redissolution; salt crystals begin to form in most beautiful patterns. Again, it would seem to the onlooker that at this point the solution has acquired a creative ability to give birth to special crystal structures. Actually this is a quantitative relationship, the balance between deposit and dissolution.

Let us return now to the evolution of the nervous system in animals. We know that the nervous system enables animals to adapt themselves to their environment with the help of their sense organs and their memory. In fact we know that animals "learn" from experience, and that this learning capacity is an important factor in survival. Yet a large part of animal behavior is based upon "instincts," it is part of the biological inheritance.

When man evolved from the animal kingdom, something new must have happened. We contend that this new element is based solely upon a quantitative difference in the nervous system. By an increase in this system nature established a new type of evolution which has broken and will break all rules established in the previous evolutionary periods.

The elements of the new evolution are all present in the animal world: memory and learning and perhaps even the formation of concepts and ideas. Only, as in the salt solution below the saturation point, they are yet too weak to be constructive. The attempts at learning in the animal world are mostly "dissolved" with the death of the individual. When man evolved, the constant increase in the complexity of the brain and the nervous system reached a point at which death of an individual no longer eradicated the gains that memory of experience had established. Further, the individual became able to use his brain to draw conclusions from his experiences, to reason out consequences of actions without having to perform them. He can think of what would happen under certain conditions and can prepare his actions accordingly. The development of language and memory enabled an adult individual to tell a younger person about his experience and his reasoning, and the pupil could act as if he had had the experience himself, or had carried through the reasoning. The workings of the brain became complex enough to provide for vicarious experience and vicarious reasoning and to enable man to pool the experiences and the thinking of several individuals, and eventually to accumulate experiences and thoughts from generation to generation. This accummulation was made possible by the development of concepts, of mental constructions, of abstract ideas, and of many other methods of formulation and transmission of thought, such as writing and painting (Figure 65). The difference between man and animal is analogous to the boiling and saturation

Figure 65. The storehouses of experience.

phenomena. Once the experiences collected by the species as a whole become more numerous than the experiences lost through the deaths of individuals, a new process begins, the formation of a "tradition."

At this point evolution has overcome the barrier against inheritance of acquired properties. As long as parents cannot transmit their experience to their offspring, the behavior of each new generation is based exclusively upon biological inheritance; it is based upon what is inscribed in the master plan contained in the cells. The situation is not changed even if there is some transmission of experience from one generation to the next. As long as the sum of experience lost by death is greater than, or as great as, the sum transmitted to the next generation, there is no accumulation of experience. The behavior of each generation is essentially the same and is dictated by biologically inherited properties. But if the transmission of experience between generations is large enough to cause an accumulation, the young will learn from the failures and successes of the elders, and newly acquired behavior patterns will be "inherited" not via the nucleic acids, but by word of mouth.

At this point a completely new form of evolution has begun. The behavior pattern changes much more rapidly than the biological changes in the body structure. While the latter changes are bound to the formation of new nucleic acid chains, the changes in the behavior pattern are much faster; they become established when a new way of behavior is found and transmitted by tradition to the following generations. For example, man has changed from a hunting animal to an agricultural one; from a cave dweller to a city builder; he has developed his toolmaking capacity from the carving of pointed stones to the machine factory. All this development took place in time intervals infinitely shorter than the periods in which biological changes have occurred—in which, as an example, man evolved from apelike animals. The large brain capable of thinking, the formation of concepts, the use of language and later on of writing bring about an accumulation of experiences which is no longer lost when an individual dies, but which is developed further with every new generation.

Once the critical number of nerve cells is reached and this stage of development attained, the further course is set and will develop at a constantly accelerating pace. Again the analogue of crystal formation in a saturated solution of salt is relevant. Crystal formation starts best from surfaces of other crystals. The first one formed has no such surface available, so it must take a relatively long time to form the first small crystal. But the next structures are formed at the surfaces of previously formed crystals. This availability makes for a rapid increase in the speed of formation. The greater the number of crystals formed, the greater are the opportunities for new formation. The same principle applies, then, to the formation of tradition. At the beginning, when mankind first acquired the possibility of developing it, the formation was very slow. Once started, however, it grew with increasing vigor and differentiation.

Tradition takes forms that are not always favorable to the species. If, however, measures are found which are favorable—like, for example, agriculture, the exploitation of metals, etc.—these measures initiate a new way of life within a few generations, and bring about that sudden change in behavior that is typically human.

Science is just one of these new measures or attitudes which grew from the accumulation of ideas and experiences. It took many generations to disentangle the vast number of observations, to separate apparent connections from real ones, to distinguish superstition from scientific fact. But once a systematic method for recognizing facts was found, the scientific revolution of the last 300 years could get under way. There is no doubt that science constitutes an important step in the new kind of evolution which began with the formation of tradition.

So far, of course, it is only the pattern of behavior and thinking that is transmitted from one generation to the other. The body structure is still reproduced in the old-fashioned animal way of propagation, and this leaves it unchanged for many generations. But who can tell? Nobody can exclude positively the possibility of a development like that portended in Aldous Huxley's *Brave New World*. It may become possible to change at will the nucleic acids which determine the development of the species. Our knowledge of the mechanism of propagation is still very limited, but it grows dangerously fast, and human interference with the hereditary structure of germ cells is not altogether out of sight. If this aim is achieved, the planned inheritance of desirable properties of the body will be within reach.

Even without having attained this ambitious aim, the new evolution has left its mark on the planet and interferes everywhere, in an ever increasing way, with the mechanism of the previous type of evolution. Man creates new races of animals by crossbreeding and purposeful selection. The natural evolution of the animal world will never again proceed in the old way. When a new development in nature is discovered by man, it is channeled into some special direction. The times are over in which nature alone developed its own forms, slowly, by trial and error, undisturbed over many generations. No longer do we rely upon chance to produce mutations and new forms and ways of life, with man as a happy onlooker. We now take it upon ourselves to develop nature and our own species. This is an arduous task, full of pitfalls and responsibilities. We assumed this burden only a short time ago, and nobody should be astonished if we blunder now and then. After all, nature blundered in the previous evolution, when mammoths and dinosaurs acquired larger and longer dimensions until they were given up as dismal failures. We must proceed by trial and error, just as nature did. The pace of the new evolution by tradition, however, is infinitely faster than that of the old evolution by inheritance. Mistakes are punished immediately and cause tremendous suffering to the perpetrators and their offspring. We are responsible ourselves for what happens, and we cannot blame nature for it.

But isn't man himself part of nature? The tradition which mankind has accumulated, the ideas, concepts, myths, and religions, are all effects of nature's influence upon man in many ways. They originated through man's reaction to natural events, to the behavior of his fellow men, to the hardships of life in a difficult environment. Our bodies and the bodies of animals were shaped in the long and show process of natural selection; they bear witness to the conditions in which life developed during billions of years, when only those nucleic acids were able to survive that gave rise to a well-adapted unit. The tradition of human thinking and behavior is also a product of the environment upon man, this time upon the brain and not the nucleic acid. It evolved within the comparatively short time of about a million years.

EPILOGUE

Epilogue.   Our story of evolution has reached the present era. We have seen how life and man evolved from the original hydrogen gas, or better, how we believe today it may have happened. We gave a highly simplified account of it in order to emphasize the essential trends.

It is a development from the simple to the complicated, from un-ordered chaos to highly differentiated units, from the unorganized to the organized. This trend, however, is not shared by all matter in the universe; the more developed areas are much smaller than the less developed ones. Only a small part of the hydrogen cloud is able to form stars; in a small part of the star (the inner part) hydrogen is transformed into heavier elements; only a small part of these ele-ments is ejected into space, only a small fraction of the ejected mat-ter assembles in the form of a planet around a star, a small fraction of all planets is sufficiently near but not too near to the star, so that water stays liquid and chemical reactions can happen; only a very small part of matter on these planets forms the long chain mole-cules which are the basis of life, and only a small part of all living matter develops a brain.

Every step to higher differentiation in this development requires an abundant amount of less differentiated material. The nuclear oven in the center of the star would not be hot enough for the production of elements, were it not surrounded by vast amounts of hydrogen; life on Earth requires radiant heat which can be supplied only by a much larger body, the Sun, whose material is in a more primitive stage, since no molecule can exist at high temperature.

It is often said that science has displaced man and his Earth from the center of the universe, where he fondly had believed himself to be, and relegates him to some unimportant place. Our Sun is only a small and undistinguished starlet in a corner of the enormous expanses of our galaxy, with many other stars like it. What is more, there are probably quite a number of other stars with planets where life has developed. These might be depressing thoughts for some.

But it may also have a different significance. The vastness of the universe, the billions of stars and the space between them are necessary conditions for the development of matter from simple, unordered particles to atoms and molecules and finally to the large aggregates which form animals and sentient beings. The spots at which matter acquires more differentiated shape are very few and selected. They must be considered as the most developed and most outstanding parts of the universe, the parts where matter was able to make fuller use of its potentialities. We find ourselves, therefore, in a very privileged and central position, since our Earth is one of these spots. There might be other places where the development has gone much further even than here, but on the Earth's surface life has developed and produced a thinking species. Nature is reflected in the thoughts of these beings.

But it is not a simple reflection. In man's brain the impressions from outside are not merely registered; they produce concepts and ideas. They are the imprint of the external world upon the human brain. Therefore, it is not unusual that, after a long period of searching and erring, some of the concepts and ideas in human thinking should have come gradually closer to the fundamental laws of this world, that some of our thinking should reveal the true structure of atoms and the true movements of the stars. Nature, in the form of man, begins to recognize itself.

INDEX